THE PAPER MUSEUM OF CASSIANO DAL POZZO

SERIES B ~ PART SIX

FLORA: THE *ERBARIO MINIATO* AND OTHER DRAWINGS

THE PAPER MUSEUM OF CASSIANO DAL POZZO

A CATALOGUE RAISONNÉ

Drawings and Prints
in the Royal Library at Windsor Castle,
the British Museum, the Institut de France
and other Collections

General Editors
Arthur MacGregor and Jennifer Montagu

Editor, Series A ~ Antiquities and Architecture
Amanda Claridge

Managing Editor
Kate Owen

Project Co-ordinator
Rea Alexandratos

Patrons and Sponsors
Accademia dei Lincei
Académie des Inscriptions et Belles-Lettres
British Academy
Getty Grant Program
Monument Trust
Olivetti
Royal Collection Trust
Warburg Institute

SERIES B ~ NATURAL HISTORY

PART SIX

FLORA
THE *ERBARIO MINIATO* AND OTHER DRAWINGS

VOLUME TWO

Fabio Garbari and Lucia Tongiorgi Tomasi

Volume editors

Brent Elliott and Martin Clayton

The Royal Collection

in association with

Harvey Miller Publishers

First published 2007 by
Royal Collection Enterprises Ltd,
St James's Palace, London SW1A 1BQ

www.royalcollection.org.uk

This catalogue has been published with the financial assistance and the support of the Fondazione Cassa di Risparmio di Alessandria

FONDAZIONE
CASSA DI RISPARMIO DI ALESSANDRIA

ISBN 978-1-905375-20-2 (Volume 1)
978-1-905375-21-9 (Volume 2)
978-1-905375-18-9 (Set)

British Library Cataloguing in Publication Data
A catalogue record for this book is available from the British Library.

Composition by Libanus Press, Marlborough, Wiltshire
Monochrome and colour origination by Grafikon, Belgium
Printed and bound in Belgium by Grafikon

Distributed by Brepols Publishers, London/Turnhout; www.brepols.net

CONTENTS

VOLUME TWO

CATALOGUE

The *Erbario Miniato*: entries 155–211

Loose drawings from a companion volume to the *Erbario Miniato*: entries 212–277

Other dal Pozzo botanical drawings: entries 278–293

155. Caterpillar plant, *Scorpiurus vermiculatus* L.

Erbario Miniato, fol. 155 (RL 27845)

NUMBERING: *652*

VERSO: offset of **149**

The caterpillar plant is a herbaceous annual of the family Fabaceae, common in Spain, Italy and North Africa in dry meadows and open scrubland, at altitudes from sea level to 1,200m. The entire plant is shown, from its long, slender taproot to its fruit – long, curled and knobbed pods growing in pairs at the ends of long peduncles. The smooth, reddish-brown stem begins branching directly at its base, with lanceolate leaves that narrow markedly at their base, to form long fruiting peduncles.

The curious form of the mature fruit, reminiscent of the scorpion's tail, suggested to Linnaeus the genus name *Scorpiurus*. Like the heliotrope (**147**) and annual scorpion vetch (**154**), the contorted pods were believed to be an antidote to scorpion stings. An offset of the drawing is found on the verso of **148**, and on the verso of the present sheet is an offset of **149**, indicating that **155** was originally positioned between **148** and **149**, and suggesting that **155** was initially identified as a type of heliotrope.

652
155.

156. Grape, *Vitis vinifera* L.

Erbario Miniato, fol. 156 (RL 27846)

NUMBERING: *653*

ANNOTATION: *Le frondi delle Viti, mittigano, inpiastrati, i dolori del' corpo* [Mattioli: *capo*] / *beuto il loro succo, giova ali stomachi deboli; il licore de le vite* / *che e' a' modo di gonna* [M: *gomma*] *che si ritrova nel tronco de detta vite* / *beuto con vino caccia fuori le pietre* / ~~*Uva*~~ *Lua fresca conturba il corpo, la manco nociva è quella che dopo che* / *e' stata colta e' a' piccata. e' utile allo stomaco* / *il vino negro. e' grosso è malagevole da degirire. nutrisce la colora* [M: *carne*]. *e' fa imbriacare.* / *il vermiglio. mezzano de colore. tra il bianco e' il negro. ha parimente le sue* / *forze mezane. tra le doi sorte. 1375;* ~~*N.º 4*~~. ('Vine leaves applied externally mitigate the pains of the body [Mattioli: head]. Its juice when drunk is beneficial for weak stomachs; the liquor of the vine, which is a [gum]-like substance found in the trunk of the said vine, eliminates kidney stones when drunk with wine. The fresh fruit perturbs the body. The least noxious is that which has been hung to dry after it has been harvested. It is good for the stomach. Black wine is heavy and difficult to digest, nourishes choler [M: the flesh] and induces drunkenness. Vermiglio [wine], which is halfway in colour between white and black, has effects similarly halfway between the two sorts. 1375; ~~No. 4~~'). [From Mattioli 1568, pp. 1375, 1379]

Vitis vinifera is a woody perennial that grows at altitudes from sea level to 800m and sometimes even higher in the dry valleys of the Alps (see also **157–159**). Its original habitat is unknown, but it has been cultivated for thousands of years in Mediterranean and sub-Mediterranean climates. The grape was cultivated 5,000 or 6,000 years ago in Egypt, perhaps from vinestocks originating in the Near East, and recent palynological studies have demonstrated its presence on the Tuscan coast as early as 4000 BC. Viticulture seems to have begun around 2000 BC in Sicily; from Italy it spread throughout the Mediterranean and by 1500 BC grapes were grown all over the Near East and the Aegean. In Greece the grape was closely linked to the cult of Dionysus. In ancient times wine was flavoured with resins or aromatic herbs, and diluted with water before being consumed. For centuries after the fall of the Roman Empire viticulture was largely confined to the religious orders, and it was only during the Renaissance that the vine was again widely cultivated beyond the confines of the monasteries.

The artist has portrayed a leaf and a bunch of ripe grapes hanging from a vine. The shoot is light in colour with faint reddish patches. The broad leaf with its toothed margins is somewhat loosely sketched; in contrast the cluster of fruit has been drawn with great care. *Vitis vinifera* is illustrated on p. 1376 of the *Discorsi*, and the annotations are drawn from Dioscorides' three chapters on the 'Vite vinifera', on the grape ('Della uva') and on the nature of wine ('Della natura del vino').

156
653
Le frondi delle Viti, mittigano, impiastrati, i dolori del corpo
beuto il loro succo, gioua ali stomachi deboli; il licore de le uite
che è a modo di gomma che si ritroua nel tronco de detta uite
beuto con uino caccia fuori le pietre
Vua fresca conturba il corpo, la manco nociua è quella che dopo che
è stata colta è a' seccata. è utile allo stomaco
il uino negro. è grosso. è malageuole da degirire. nutrisce la colora. è fa imbriacare.
il uermiglio. mezzano de colore. tra il bianco è il negro. ha parimente le sue
forze mezane. tra le doi sorte. 1375
N.o 1.

157. Grape, *Vitis vinifera* L.

Erbario Miniato, fol. 157 (RL 27847)

NUMBERING: *654*

ANNOTATION: *Le frondi delle Vite / e' parimenti i caprioli / triti mittigano, impiastrati / con polenta, le infiamagioni / e' dolori dello stomaco, il che giovano / ancora le fronde sole como cose / frigide, e' costretive, beuto il succo de le fronde / giova alla disenteria, allo sputo del sangue, agli stomachi deboli, e' alla pitito / corrotto, delle donne gravide, il che fanno ancora i, caprioli, infusi nel laccqua / e' beuti, la cenere de i sarmenti, e' de i venacci, medica, impiastrata con aceto, / alle nascentie del sedere, e' a' i thimi: giova alle membra smosse, e' ai morsi / delle vipere, fassini impiastro alle infiamagione della milza, con olio rosato / ruta e' aceto, 1375* ('Vine leaves, and similarly the tendrils, ground and applied with pearl barley, reduce irritations and pains of the stomach. Also beneficial for these are the leaves alone since they are cooling and constrictive. Drinking the juice from the leaves is good for dysentery, for the spitting of blood, for weak stomachs and for the cravings of pregnant women. The tendrils have the same effects when infused in water and drunk. The ashes of the branches and of the pips, applied with vinegar, medicate anal growths and fleshy excrescences. It is beneficial for dislocated limbs and for bites from vipers. A poultice is made from it with rose oil, rue and vinegar for inflammations of the spleen. 1375'). [From Mattioli 1568, p. 1375]

VERSO: offset of **159**

This drawing shows part of a vine (see **156**) with a leaf and a cluster of light-coloured grapes hanging from a node. The tri-palmate leaf is yellowish-green with deeply toothed margins. The annotation copies in full a passage in the *Discorsi* on the 'vite vinifera' that was already copied in part in **156**, the only instance of repetition of notes in the *Erbario*.

158. Grape, *Vitis vinifera* L.

Erbario Miniato, fol. 158 (RL 27848)

Watermark: Anchor 30

Here the artist provides a somewhat summary rendition of a cluster of grapes (see **156**) with a leaf. The leaf is divided into three deep lobes with toothed margins and a long petiole; its upper surface is deep yellow while the lower surface is a light green.

159. Grape, *Vitis vinifera* L.

Erbario Miniato, fol. 159 (RL 27849)

Watermark: Fleur de lys 17

NUMBERING: *655*

ANNOTATION: *Agresto*

This drawing shows a vine with two leaves and a small cluster of green grapes (see **156**). The shoot is reddish-brown with green patches at its nodes. The leaves have broad lobes and deeply toothed margins.

The single-word annotation probably comes from p. 1379 of the *Discorsi*, Dioscorides' chapter entitled 'Dell'Omphacio, cioè Agresto' ('Agresto' being Mattioli's addition, as he comments that Dioscorides' 'Omphacio' is 'popularly called by us *Agresto*'). *Omphacio* and *agresto* were the juice of unripe grapes (verjuice) used as a condiment and medicine.

634

Le frondi delle Vite
e' parimente i caprioli
triti mittigano, impiastrati
con poleata, le infiamagioni
e' dolori dello stomaco, il che giouano
ancora le fronde sole. como cose
frigide, e' costretiue, beuto il succo de le fronde
gioua alla disenteria, allo sputo del sangue, agli stomacchi deboli, e' alla pitito
corrotto, delle donne grauide, il che fanno ancora i caprioli, infusi nel l'acqua
e' beuti, la cenere de i sarmenti, e' de i uenacci, medica, impiastrata con aceto,
alle nascentie del sedere, e' a' i thimi: gioua alle membra smosse, e' ai morsi
delle uipere, fassini impiastro alle infiamagione della milza, con olio rosato
uita e' aceto. 1375

158.

655
159
Agresto

160. Chinese rhubarb, *Rheum palmatum* L. 1758–9

Erbario Miniato, fol. 160 (RL 27850)

Cut out from two joined sheets and inlaid

Watermark: Hand 2

NUMBERING: *656*

VERSO: black chalk outline of the drawing

This striking drawing shows a root of the Chinese rhubarb, a perennial of the family Polygonaceae. It is common in China, growing in mountainous regions at altitudes from 800m to 1,500m, and may be found in cultivated and wild forms in other parts of the world. The Chinese rhubarb has been used as a purgative in the Far East for thousands of years. It reached Europe in the Middle Ages (see Turner 1938, p. 360). Mattioli devotes many pages in his *Terzo libro* to the characteristics and properties of different types of rhubarb – *medicina benedetta, eccellente, et solenne* ('blessed, excellent and outstanding medicine') – but he is not cited here.

The drawing includes only part of the broad tuberous root of the plant, with a rough, dark brown surface and a white interior, and may be a later addition to the *Erbario*. It has been cut from another sheet and laid into the page the wrong way up, and is a copy of a large drawing in the manuscript *Icones variarum plantarum* (comp. fig. 160), created by the artist Filippo Paladini (1544–1608) for the Franciscan friar Francesco Malocchi, who served as director of the Giardino dei Semplici of Pisa from 1596 to 1613. Paladini worked at the Botanic Garden of Pisa in 1602–4, while Cassiano dal Pozzo was studying at the university there, and it is just possible that this drawing was acquired by Cassiano while he was a student and added by him to the *Erbario* after he acquired Cesi's library. Alternatively, the drawing may have been acquired by Heckius in 1604, when he travelled to Pisa to pay his respects to the celebrated physician Gerolamo Mercuriale. While in Pisa, Malocchi took Heckius on a tour of the university's natural history collection – *Museum miris naturalibus comptum elegantissimo ordine dispositum* ('a museum of natural wonders laid out in the most elegant order'), as Heckius wrote afterwards (Gabrieli 1989, II, p. 1107).

Comp. fig. 160. Chinese rhubarb (*Rheum palmatum*). Filippo Paladini, *Icones variarum plantarum*, folios 32v–33r. Pisa, BU, MS 465

959

161. Holly, *Ilex aquifolium* L.

Erbario Miniato, fol. 161 (RL 27851)

Watermark: Eagle (unidentified)

NUMBERING: *657*

VERSO: offset of **208**

Holly is an evergreen shrub of the family Aquifoliaceae that thrives in fertile, well-watered terrain, generally at altitudes from 200m to 800m (although in Sicily, in the Madonie mountains, there is a well-known forest consisting entirely of holly at an altitude of 1,300m). It is found throughout southern and central Europe, North Africa and Turkey.

This drawing shows a cultivated form of the plant with spineless leaves. Though today most spineless forms are derived from the *Ilex* × *altaclerensis* hybrids originally bred in the nineteenth century, such forms arise from time to time as sports. The stem is thick, smooth and sinuous, the leaves oval in form with entire margins and acute apices. The white flowers at the end of the stem are still in the bud. The fruit consists of reddish-orange berries growing from short, erect peduncles.

Holly, which today is associated with the festivities of Christmas, was in Roman times used as an amulet in the rites preceding the winter solstice. Its leaves, with their tough spines and perennial green colour, were a symbol of protection, survival and prosperity, while the fruit, which matures in the depths of winter, promised the rebirth of the sun and a prosperous year to come. Mattioli wrote that the spiny branches could be used to protect salted meat from mice (*I Discorsi*, p. 179), and thus one name for the plant in Italian was *pungitopo maggiore* ('greater mouse-pricker'; cf. the butcher's broom, **113**). The leaves were once used medicinally, but the berries are quite poisonous.

161
657

162. Field maple, *Acer campestre* L.

Erbario Miniato, fol. 162 (RL 27852)

Watermark: Eagle 15

NUMBERING: *658*

ANNOTATION: *~~Ornell~~ erniglossa; Acera magiore / detta volgarmente stucchio.* ('*~~Ornell~~. erniglossa.* Greater maple, commonly called *stucchio*.')

The field maple is a tree of the family Aceraceae which is native to Europe, the Caucasus region and North Africa, and has become naturalized in the rest of the world. It thrives in fertile soil at altitudes from sea level to 800m.

The small branch in this drawing is covered with smooth grey bark. The leaves, which grow from long, slender, flexible petioles, are palmate with five lobes and irregular margins. The three central lobes are well developed, while the two proximal ones are still in an early stage, although their central vein can be clearly seen. The green fruits (samaras) are contained in light-coloured, almost transparent paired wings. At lower right is a separate yellowing leaf.

162.

650

ermiglossa

Acera· magiore
detta uolgarmente Stucchio.

163. Laurustinus, *Viburnum tinus* L.

Erbario Miniato, fol. 163 (RL 27853)

Watermark: Crown 48

NUMBERING: *659*

ANNOTATION: *Lauro Salvatico. o' vero Sambucella detto dal vulgo / ha ô vero participa de la qualita del lauro; N:º ~~340~~* ('Wild laurel or popularly *Sambucella*. It has, or it shares, the qualities of the laurel. No. ~~340~~')

The laurustinus is a shrub of the family Caprifoliaceae. It is common in oak and evergreen forests at altitudes from sea level to 800m in southern Europe and North Africa, and is a typical plant of the *maquis*, the scrubland of southern Europe and the Mediterranean. Of the many species of the genus *Viburnum*, the laurustinus is of particular interest to gardeners because it is an evergreen which blossoms in winter, and it was much used for hedges in the seventeenth century.

The stem is erect, thick and woody. The leaves are broadly lanceolate with entire margins and acute apices. The flowers consist of white corollas made up of five petals with white stamens that are longer than the petals themselves. The pear-shaped, dark blue berries are carried on lax corymbs.

659

Lauro Saluatico . ó uero Sambucella detto dal uulgo
Ea ó uero participa de la qualita del Lauro .

N:° 340

164. Heather, *Erica* sp.

Erbario Miniato, fol. 164 (RL 27854)

Watermark: Bird 20

NUMBERING: *660*

ANNOTATION: [cut] *Fiori de Scopo* ('*Scopo* flowers')

This simplified drawing shows a slender stem, pinkish in colour and branching at its apex. Each branch, which is subtended by narrow linear bracts, carries at its apex a dense raceme of small pink flowers. The leaves, the lower part of the plant and the root system are not shown. The artist does not furnish enough detail to allow an exact identification, but it appears to be a species of heather. In the index at the end of the *Erbario* the plant is identified (as in the annotation) as a 'fior di scopo'; in Tuscany *scopo* was the common name for besom heath, *Erica scoparia*. Heathers were not treated as garden plants until the eighteenth century.

660
164.

165. Tobacco, *Nicotiana tabacum* L.

Erbario Miniato, fol. 165 (RL 27855)

Watermark: Eagle (unidentified)

NUMBERING: *661*

ANNOTATION: *Tabaccho. overo Erba / santa portata da lindie / nuove. il Matiuolo no*[*n*] */ la' conosciuta.* ('Tobacco or holy plant brought from the [West] Indies. It was not known to Mattioli.')

VERSO: offset of **164**

LITERATURE: Gabrieli 1929, pp. 533–4 (fig. 1)

The tobacco plant is a member of the family Solanaceae, native to South America. The stem of this specimen is thick, slightly sinuous and tapering at its apex. The alternate amplexicaul leaves are broadly elliptical in shape with scalloped margins and acute apices. The central vein can clearly be seen, particularly on the undersides of the blades. At the distal end of the stem are several flowers carried on short peduncles, some in full bloom, others still closed. The calyx, which extends for one-third the length of the corolla, appears to be deeply lobed because it is made up of five sepals that are united at their base and along half of their length. The funnel-shaped corolla is light grey except at its opening, which is divided into broad pink lobes.

Tobacco was one of the most important plants to be brought back from the New World by European explorers – Columbus discovered the plant on his first expedition to the West Indies in October 1492. It was used by the native peoples of the Americas for purposes ranging from a dessert to the induction of trances, although the species used for this latter purpose was *Nicotiana rustica*, which contains much higher levels of nicotine than *N. tabacum*. The name 'tobacco' seems first to have been used in Europe in 1535 by Gonzalo Fernandez de Oviedo y Valdés. In 1561 Cardinal Prospero di Santa Croce, who was serving as apostolic nuncio in Lisbon, brought back with him some seeds that were planted in the Vatican gardens and for this reason the plant was called *erba di Santa Croce* (as in the *Erbario*'s index) or *erba santa* (as it is named in the annotation here). The name *Nicotiana* was coined by Daléchamps in 1586 and refers to Jean Nicot of Nîmes (1530–1600), who introduced tobacco to the French royal court after serving as the French consul in Lisbon.

By the beginning of the seventeenth century the harmful effects of the plant were already being debated – one of the earliest anti-smoking publications was *A Counterblaste to Tobacco*, written in 1604 by James I of England, who reputedly became ill after his first attempt at smoking. All the green parts of the tobacco plant contain alkaloids which decompose into ammonia and nicotine when heated. Nicotine is absorbed through the skin and the mucous membranes, and can cause paralysis or even death in high doses. Until the development of modern pesticides, tobacco was the gardener's principal fumigant for glasshouses. The plant was employed against a variety of ills from ulcers to (ironically) coughing and asthma, but such medicinal applications have long been abandoned.

While Mattioli does not mention tobacco in his *Discorsi*, he possessed a remarkable pen-and-ink drawing of the plant (*c.* 1567, private collection) which had been sent to him by a colleague who annotated the sheet: 'Herba della Reina venuta dal Peru' ('Queen's plant that came from Peru'; see Toresella 1992, pp. 46–7).

661
165.
Tabaccho ouero herba
santa portata da lindie
nuoue. il Matiuolo nō
la' Conosciuta.

166. Wild tobacco, *Nicotiana rustica* L.

Erbario Miniato, fol. 166 (RL 27856)

Watermark: Eagle 15

NUMBERING: *662*

ANNOTATION: *Unaltro tabacco. p*[*er*] *il dolore de li denti. cosa rarissima. / metendo una piloletta al dente che duole de la sua fresca erba.* ('Another tobacco. For toothache a most rare thing [i.e. cure], placing a small pill of the fresh plant on the tooth that hurts.')

The wild tobacco is native to Central and South America (Mexico, Ecuador, Peru and Bolivia), where, like other species of the genus *Nicotiana* (see **165**), it was cultivated for ritual use. It was probably the first species of the genus to be introduced to Europe.

The stem of this specimen is erect and smooth. The olive-green leaves with dark green veins, elliptical in form with entire margins and blunt apices, grow alternately along the stem on petioles one-third the length of the leaf blades. The flowers are carried on slender, curving peduncles and have deeply lobed calyxes covered with downy hairs. The greenish-yellow corollas are tube-shaped and end in five lobes; the reproductive structures are not visible. The plant's grey taproot divides into three roots that are densely branched at their ends.

662

Vnaltro tabacco. p il dolore de li denti. cosa rarissima.
metendo una pilloletta al dente che duolo. de la sua fresca erba.

167. Cut-leaved self-heal, *Prunella laciniata* (L.) L. 1762–3

Erbario Miniato, fol. 167 (RL 27857)

NUMBERING: *663*

ANNOTATION: *TERTIANARIA*

Self-heal is a perennial of the family Lamiaceae, common around the Mediterranean in open arid ground at altitudes from sea level to 1,400m. The stem of this specimen is robust and sinuous with leaves growing in opposite pairs. Near the base of the plant the leaves are elliptical in form with entire margins; higher up on the stem they are divided into laciniate lobes with acute apices. The flowers at the apex are borne on short verticillasters. The corollas are cream-coloured and bilabial, but no further details can be distinguished. The plant has a short, thickly branching taproot.

In the Renaissance the names *prunella* and *brunella* were used interchangeably. Here it is called 'tertianaria', perhaps suggesting that it was thought useful for tertian fever, i.e. malaria. Given the sickle-shaped profile of the corolla and the serrated edge of the leaves, the doctrine of signatures indicated its use to heal cuts, but in reality it has no medicinal applications.

663

TERTIANARIA

168. Unidentified plant

Erbario Miniato, fol. 168 (RL 27858)

Watermark: Eagle 18

NUMBERING: *664*

ANNOTATION: *~~Herba Valeria~~*; *Piede de sparvier*[–] ('~~Valeria plant~~; foot of the sparrowhawk')

This drawing shows a plant with its root system. The stem is erect and covered with stiff hairs. The leaves are alternate and elliptical in form, with acute apices and four or five pointed teeth along each side. The plant ends in a long taproot with little branching.

The names given in the annotation here are not listed in the index to *I Discorsi*. Mattioli used the name 'Valeriana' in his commentary on Dioscorides' 'Phu'; the illustrations of the 'Phu' on pp. 42–6 of the *Discorsi* are all *Valeriana* spp., though the details shown here are insufficient to identify the specimen as a valerian.

168
664
Herba Valerra
Prede de sparuier

169. Scarlet pimpernel, *Anagallis arvensis* L.

Erbario Miniato, fol. 169 (RL 27859)

Watermark: Eagle 15

NUMBERING: *665*

ANNOTATION: *limodorum tritici; Spetie de Alsine. è da altri, Galinelle, fiamma de / grano, no*[*n*] *scritta dal matiolo.* ('Corn *limodorum*. A type of chickweed, called by others little chicken, or wheat flame. Not mentioned by Mattioli.')

The scarlet pimpernel is a herbaceous annual of the family Primulaceae. Originally native to central and southern Europe and temperate regions of Asia, it is now naturalized all over the world, infesting fields of grain (particularly wheat) and growing in shrubland and uncultivated terrain at altitudes from sea level to 1,200m.

This drawing illustrates a flowering stem at a right angle to its long, slender root. The leaves have been erroneously shown growing alternately along the stem (they are in reality opposite). Lanceolate with entire margins, each leaf subtends a small branch bearing flowers with long peduncles and purple corollas made up of five obovate petals. The petals have fallen away from two of the flowers, exposing the calyx which consists of five linear sepals. The fruits, which are typical pyxes, can also be seen.

The scarlet pimpernel was familiar to the Greeks and Romans for its medicinal properties; according to the masters of the medieval *Schola Salernitana* it could be used to treat eye problems, epilepsy and a tired constitution. Although it may irritate the skin and mucosal passages, it is an effective expectorant and may be used for the treatment of bedsores and infected wounds.

169.

665

Limodorum tritici.

Spetie de Alsine. è da altri, Galinelle, fiamma de grano. nō scritta dal matiolo.

170. Annual gypsophila, *Gypsophila muralis* L.

Erbario Miniato, fol. 170 (RL 27860)

NUMBERING: *666*

ANNOTATION: *OSTEOCOLLON*

VERSO: offset of **205**

The annual gypsophila is a member of the Caryophyllaceae family, diffuse in northern Europe including the northern regions of Italy. It grows in damp sandy soil, rice fields and along forest paths from sea level to an altitude of 500m. It has been cultivated since the eighteenth century as a modest garden plant, but does not have any medicinal properties.

The stem is slender, sinuous and branching at its base. The long, narrow leaves are opposite, sessile and slightly amplexicaul with entire margins. Growing at the apex of each branch is a single flower whose calyx is made up of sepals that are fused at their base and elongated and toothed at the throat. The corolla is composed of five rounded pink petals. The reproductive structures are not clearly visible and the artist has not shown the fruit. The root system is highly branching.

The generic name *Gypsophila* is derived from the Greek γύψος (*gypsos*), 'gypsum', and φιλία (*philia*), 'love', because the plant flourishes in soil or walls with a high gypsum content. The name 'osteocollon' used here, presumably from the Greek όστεον (*osteon*), 'bone', and κολλάω (*kollao*), 'to glue', may refer to the plant's use in the preparation of casts for broken bones.

170.
OSTEOCOILON
666

171. Unidentified plant

Erbario Miniato, fol. 171 (RL 27861)

NUMBERING: *667*

VERSO: offset of **169**

This drawing shows two flowering stems of a plant belonging to the family Lamiaceae; it cannot be more precisely identified though it is probably a cultivated variety. Each specimen has an erect, slightly sinuous stem that terminates in a raceme thickly covered with small flowers that are white in the left-hand specimen and pink in the other. The leaves are opposite and lanceolate with short petioles, entire margins and acute apices.

172. European cranberry, *Vaccinium oxycoccus* L.

Erbario Miniato, fol. 172 (RL 27862)

NUMBERING: *668*

ANNOTATION: [cut] *Spetie de fana*[*ce*] ('A type of *fanace*')

VERSO: offset of **204**

The European cranberry belongs to the family Ericaceae and grows in swamps and peat bogs at altitudes from 800m to 2,000m in central and northern Europe, in the temperate mountainous regions of Asia and in North America. In Italy this plant can now be found only in nature reserves in the Alpine region of Trento, though as late as the 1930s it was still fairly common in the Sibolla marshes near Lucca, where the fruit was gathered and used to make preserves. In Russia the species is commercially cultivated.

The stem of this specimen is slender and flexible with an adventitious rootlet. The alternate, olive-green leaves are elliptical in form with short petioles and lighter coloured undersides. The plant's shiny red berry (also shown in the detail to lower left) grows from a slender peduncle; the flowers are not shown.

The ancient name for the cranberry, *Vaccinium* (which can be found in Virgil), may have originated from *vacca* ('cow'), since cattle will forage for this plant, or from *bacca* ('berry').

172.
Spetie de fanac

173. Joseph's coat, *Amaranthus tricolor* L.

Erbario Miniato, fol. 173 (RL 27863)

Watermark: Fleur de lys 51

NUMBERING: *669*

ANNOTATION: *Herba Maraviglia* ('Marvel plant')

The Joseph's coat, a species belonging to the family Amaranthaceae, probably originated in the tropical regions of Asia but is now naturalized in many parts of Europe and cultivated as an ornamental plant all over the world. It became popular as an ornamental in Europe in the mid-sixteenth century, when its introduction caused great excitement among gardeners. John Gerard said of it: 'It farre exceedeth my skill to describe the beautie and excellencie of this rare plant called *Floramor* . . . I cannot with words set forth, such are the sundry mixtures of colours that Nature hath bestowed in her greatest jolitie, upon this floure' (Gerard 1597, p. 255). This enthusiasm, which later waned, explains the name inscribed here.

The thick, smooth stem of this specimen ends in a large number of alternate, lanceolate, strongly veined leaves on long petioles. The leaves are strikingly coloured, the part closest to the petiole a bright orange-yellow or red and the other half a vivid green. The flowers, fruit and roots are not shown. The generic name comes from the Greek αμάραντος (*amarantos*), 'never fading', and was used for a group of plants that retained their colour as dried or cut flowers. The identity of the classical amaranth is now uncertain, and several species that were included in the genus *Amaranthus* are now regarded as belonging to different genera such as *Celosia* and *Gomphrena*.

173
669
Herba Marauiglia

174. Field cow-wheat, *Melampyrum arvense* L.

Erbario Miniato, fol. 174 (RL 27864)

NUMBERING: *670*

ANNOTATION: *TRITICO VACCINO DA ALCUNI CODA VOLPINA* ('Cow wheat, called by some foxtail')

VERSO: offsets of **173** and **175**

The field cow-wheat is an annual species of the family Scrophulariaceae, widespread in Europe and Asia Minor, where it grows by hedgerows and in fields of grain from sea level to an altitude of 1,700m (see also **175**). All plants of the genus *Melampyrum* are hemiparasitic, obtaining some of their nutrients by photosynthesis, but also establishing a parasitic relationship with plants growing near them. When field cow-wheat infests grain fields it can seriously impair the yield, and its seeds will mix with those of the crop and impart a dark colour and bitter taste to the flour – the generic name *Melampyrum* comes from the Greek μέλας (*melas*), 'black', and πυρός (*pyros*), 'wheat'. Many of the common names for the plant (foxtail, donkey tail and so on) refer to the form of the inflorescence.

The erect stem begins branching directly at its base. The long, lanceolate leaves have deeply slashed margins forming three or four narrow segments on each side near the stem. An inflorescence springs from the apex of each branch, composed of numerous clusters of flowers that are bright red in colour with streaks of yellow along their tubular corollas. The root is sinuous with no branches.

670

TRITICO VACCINO DA ALCVNI CODA VOLPINA

175. Field cow-wheat, *Melampyrum arvense* L.

Erbario Miniato, fol. 175 (RL 27865)

Watermark: Eagle 15

NUMBERING: *671*

ANNOTATION: *Coda Volpina* ('Foxtail')

This drawing shows the upper portion of the field cow-wheat (see **174**). The erect, smooth stem bears three pairs of leaves, the lowest pair long and narrow with entire margins, the upper pairs deeply toothed near the base. A slender branch with young leaves grows from the second axil. The distal portion of the tube-shaped corolla is brown, while the rest of the flower is yellowish-pink.

176. Red coral, *Corallium rubrum* L. 1758–9 (Lam. 1801)

Erbario Miniato, fol. 176 (RL 27866)

Watermark: Fleur de lys 52

NUMBERING: *672*

ANNOTATION: *Corrallina rubra. 1123 nel Eicones; Scopo Marino, no*[*n*] *scritto dal Matiolo* ('Red coral. 1123 in the *Eicones*. Sea broom, not mentioned by Mattioli'). [From Tabernaemontanus 1590, p. 1123]

VERSO: offset of **175**

Corals were often included in antique and Renaissance herbals (including Tabernaemontanus's *Eicones plantarum*, cited here) because they were thought to be plants. The French botanist Bernard de Jussieu (1699–1777) was the first to identify corals and madrepores (stony corals) as animals, removing them from the ranks of plants before the establishment of modern botanical nomenclature in Linnaeus's *Species plantarum* (1753). Coral was believed to have medicinal applications, and an *electuarium diacorallion* could be found in many pharmacies.

177. Crosswort, *Cruciata laevipes* Opiz

Erbario Miniato, fol. 177 (RL 27867)

NUMBERING: *673*

ANNOTATION: *Crociata*

The crosswort is a herbaceous species of the family Rubiaceae, found in forests and underbrush throughout Europe. The drawing shows only the upper part of the plant. The erect stem is covered with stiff hairs and has sessile, lanceolate leaves arranged in whorls of decreasing size along its length. Numerous tiny pale green flowers can be seen growing on peduncles from the axils of the leaves. The genus name of the plant and its common names in many languages refer to the cross-like arrangement of the leaves on the stem. The crosswort was considered to be an effective remedy for wounds, hernias and rheumatism.

175.
611
Coda Volpina

176

672

Corallina rubra. 1123 nel Cicones

Scopo Marino, nō scritto dal Matiolo

177
673
Crociata

178. Wall germander, *Teucrium chamaedrys* L.

Erbario Miniato, fol. 178 (RL 27868)

Watermark: Eagle 18

NUMBERING: *674*

ANNOTATION: *Cerquella. herba p*[*er*] *pigliare il pesce nelle fiumare.* (‘*Cerquella*. Plant for catching fish in rivers.’)

The wall germander is a perennial of the family Lamiaceae, growing in dry pastures and oak forests at altitudes from sea level to 1,700m throughout Europe, North Africa and Asia Minor. Along the plant’s smooth slender stem grow opposite pairs of triangular leaves, with deeply toothed margins, on short petioles. The leaf is dark green in colour with a lighter coloured underside against which the veins may be clearly seen. The bright pink flowers are arranged in whorls at the axils of the leaves along the upper portion of the stem; they are not drawn in great detail, but the three lobes of the corolla’s lower lip can be seen.

The therapeutic properties of the wall germander were well known to herbalists and it is still included in the French pharmacopoeia. Mattioli illustrates and discusses the plant on pp. 865–7 of the *Discorsi*, but this is not the source of the information in the annotation regarding the wall germander’s use in catching fish. Mattioli cited both the classical names given by Dioscorides (‘Chamedrio’ and ‘Trissagine’) and the contemporary Tuscan name, *querciola*, ‘little oak’, from the toothed oak-like margins of the leaves. The name ‘Cerquella’ given here is a variant of this (from *cerqua*, an alternative to the Italian *quercia*) that is still used in Lazio.

178.
674
Cerquetta. Eerba p pigliare il pesce nelle fiumare.

179. Wood dock, *Rumex sanguineus* L.

Erbario Miniato, fol. 179 (RL 27869)

NUMBERING: *675*

ANNOTATION: *Sangue di Drago* ('Dragon's blood')

The wood dock is a member of the family Polygonaceae that is common all over Europe, where it grows in damp forests at altitudes from sea level to 1,200m, and is widely cultivated as an ornamental house plant. The principal stem of the plant is erect, thick and branching; its leaves are long and lanceolate with smooth margins and pointed apices. The flowers are arranged in eight to ten whorls along the lateral branches and at the apex of the stem, although their form cannot be clearly seen.

The generic name *Rumex* refers to the shape of the leaves of some (but not all) of the species in this genus, which resemble the point of a javelin (*rumex* was a Roman spear with a barbed head). Pliny the Elder called this group of plants 'oxalis' (see **241**), while Theophrastus used the term λάπαθος (*lapathos*), which shares the same root as the Greek λαπάσσω (*lapasso*), 'to empty', a reference to the mild laxative properties of the plant. The name 'Sangue di Drago' given here presumably refers to the colour of the stem and branches. That name is more usually used for the dragon tree, *Dracaena draco*, which contains a red resin.

179
675
Sangue di Drago

180. Slender foxtail, *Alopecurus myosuroides* Huds.

Erbario Miniato, fol. 180 (RL 27870)

NUMBERING: *676*

ANNOTATION: *Coda de Sorce; Unaltra Gramigna* ('Mouse-tail; another grass')

The slender foxtail is an annual of the family Poaceae, native to Europe, Asia Minor and the Middle East and naturalized all over the world. It grows in light, dry, calcareous soil at altitudes to 1,350m; although it provides excellent forage, it can infest grain fields and so is rarely cultivated.

The plant has an erect stem and linear leaves growing from widely spaced nodes. The bluish-green spike is composed of numerous, tightly packed spikelets whose form is not clearly distinguishable here. Both the generic name *Alopecurus* (from αλώπηξ (*alopix*), 'fox', and ουρά (*oura*), 'tail') and the specific epithet *myosuroides* (similarly from μύουρος (*myouros*), 'mouse-tail') refer to the form of the spike.

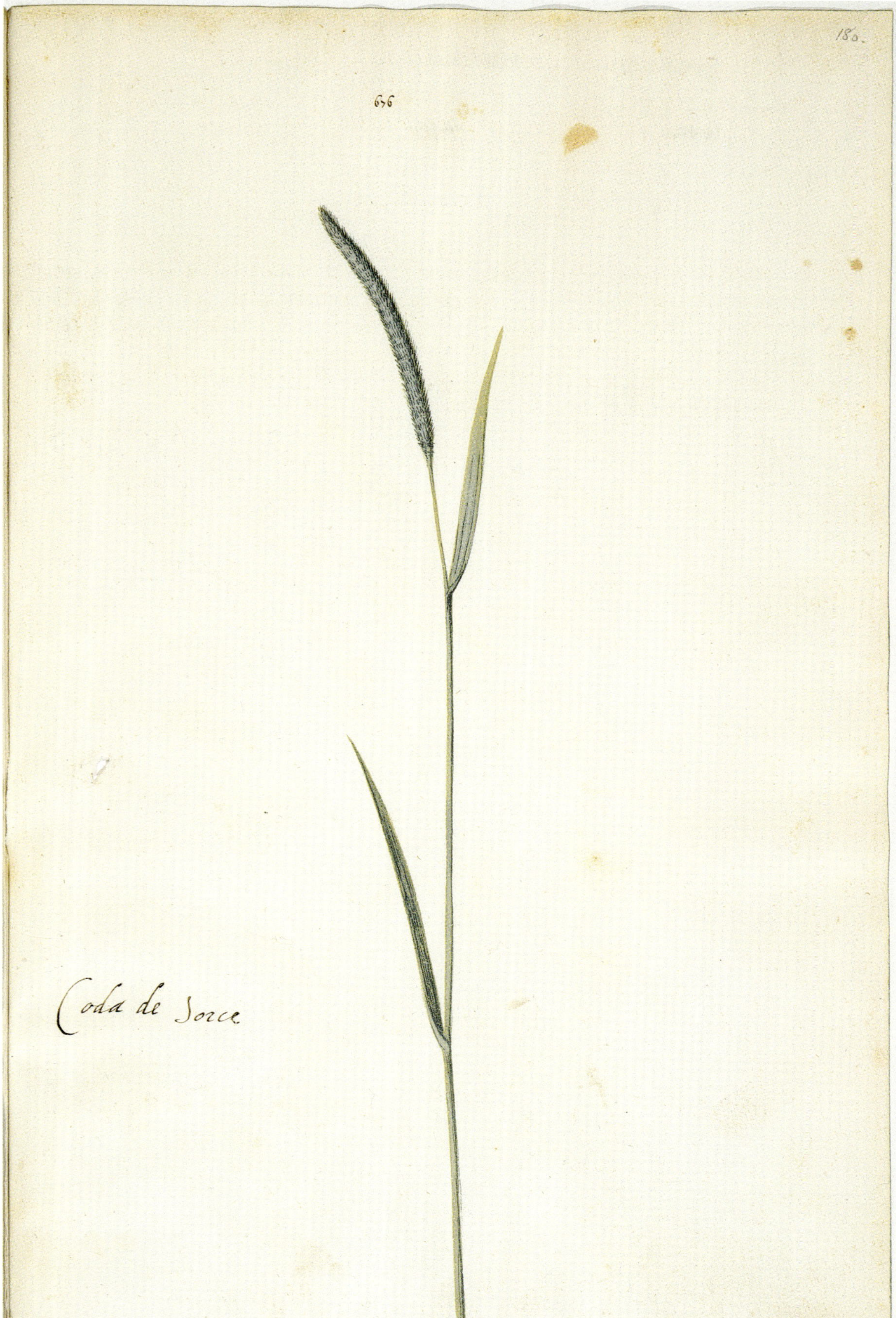
180.
656
Coda de Sorce
Vnaltra Gramigna

181. Tuberous roots of the hawkbit, *Leontodon tuberosus* L.

Erbario Miniato, fol. 181 (RL 27871)

Watermark: Fleur de lys 71

NUMBERING: *677*

ANNOTATION: *Radica de dente de cane* ('Root of the dog's tooth')

VERSO: offset of **179**

This drawing probably shows the tuberous roots of the hawkbit, a species belonging to the family Asteraceae that is diffuse in the Mediterranean. The plant grows in arid pastures and olive groves at altitudes from sea level to 1,000m. Its tubers are yellowish-brown and pear-shaped.

677

Radica de dente de cane

182. Weld, *Reseda luteola* L.

Erbario Miniato, fol. 182 (RL 27872)

NUMBERING: *678*

ANNOTATION: *Pannigella overo Bietola. la salvatica. herba rozza. se adopera p[er] / tingere li panni di colore giallo.* ('*Pannigella*, or wild beet. A coarse plant, it is used to dye cloth yellow.')

Weld is a herbaceous perennial of the family Resedaceae which may be found in southern Europe (though rarely in Italy), Egypt, Libya and temperate regions of Asia Minor. It grows in stony ground such as the gravel beds of rushing streams or the cracks of old walls, at altitudes from sea level to 1,300m.

The entire plant is shown, including the slender taproot. Long, lanceolate leaves with slightly scalloped margins grow from short petioles. A long terminal raceme carries the flowers, with short peduncles and pale yellow corollas.

The leaves contain a substance that was used to soothe insect bites, hence the generic name *Reseda*, from the Latin *redo*, 'to calm'. As the inscription states, it contains a yellow dye, and it was cultivated in France and England for this property. The roots were used to make aperitifs and vermifuges, while an infusion of the flowers was considered to be a sudorific and diuretic.

670

Pannigella ouero Bietola. la saluatica. Eerba rozza. se adopera p
tingere li panni. di colore giallo.

183. White helleborine, *Cephalanthera damasonium* (Mill.) Druce

Erbario Miniato, fol. 183 (RL 27873)

NUMBERING: *679*

ANNOTATION: [struck through: *Calceulus Marie / da altri Testeticulo Ermo / frodito*]; *Spetie de Eleborina* ('[Mary's Slipper, called by others Hermaphrodite Testicle]; Type of helleborine')

This specimen of a white helleborine (see **77**) has an erect, smooth, slender stem and veined, broad oval leaves with olive-green upper surfaces and bluish-green undersides. Three flower buds with small bracts can be seen at the apex of the stem. The root is a slender unbranched rhizome.

183.
679
da altri Testiculo Primo
prodotto,
Spetie de
Eleborina.

184. Contrayerva or tusilla, *Dorstenia contrajerva* L.

Erbario Miniato, fol. 184 (RL 27874)

Watermark: Fleur de lys 48

NUMBERING: *680*

ANNOTATION: *Radica de Herba contro herba de lindia, scritta dal Monardes* ('Root of the Indian plant [effective] against [other] plants, as written by Monardes')

VERSO: offset of **206**

Illustrated here are two tuberous rhizomes of *Dorstenia contrajerva*, a member of the family Moraceae, native to the Caribbean and northern South America. A very invasive plant, it ejects its seeds explosively to considerable distances.

This plant was first published by Nicolas Monardes in 1575 (Monardes 1575, I, pp. 80–1). In his account of new plants found in South America, he referred to a plant that was thought to heal any animal bite. Clusius, in his *Exoticorum* (1605, p. 311), translating from Monardes, named the plant 'contrayerva', and it was occasionally called *herba contra hierba*, 'herb against poisons'. The annotation here has rendered this as 'Herba contro herba', making it seem like an antidote to vegetable products rather than to poisons as a category. The plant was also illustrated in the compendium of Mexican plants prepared by Cesi and his fellow Linceans from material gathered by Francisco Hernández in the sixteenth century (see Fig. 15, p. 39).

As *contrayerva* the root of *Dorstenia* was used in the seventeenth and eighteenth centuries as a medicament, though by the end of the eighteenth century its use had declined considerably. William Woodville in 1790 said that it had become very rare in Europe, and its cultivation may never have been widespread (Woodville 1790, pp. 140–2). European knowledge of the plant was mainly limited to its rhizome, imported as a medicinal product. In Woodville's words, 'the roots of different species of Dorstenia are promiscuously gathered and exported for those of the Contrayerva', so adulteration and confusion may have reduced its perceived reliability as a medicine.

184.

600

Radica de Herba contro Eerba de Lindia, scritta dal Monardes

185. Crown daisy, *Glebionis coronaria* (L.) Cassini ex Spach

Erbario Miniato, fol. 185 (RL 27875)

NUMBERING: *681*

The crown daisy is a herbaceous annual of the family Asteraceae, native to Asia and southern Europe, naturalized throughout the world, and cultivated as a garden plant. The stem is thick, sinuous and branching, and the alternate leaves are divided into two or three feather-like leaflets with a prominent central vein. The flower head is made up of a cluster of yellow tubular flowers surrounded by white ligulate flowers marked by a splash of yellow at their base and a truncated, toothed apex.

The crown daisy was formerly classified in the genus *Chrysanthemum*. In the late twentieth century an attempt was made to break up that large and ungainly genus, and the crown daisy, formerly *Chrysanthemum coronarium*, became *Glebionis coronaria*, a name originally proposed in the 1820s by Cassini.

186. Spindle-tree, *Euonymus europaeus* L.

Erbario Miniato, fol. 186 (RL 27876)

Watermark: Crown 5

NUMBERING: *682*

The spindle-tree is a small tree belonging to the family Celastraceae, common all over Europe in forests of oak and chestnut, to an altitude of 800m. The wood is easy to work, and the English name originates from the fact that it was used to make spindles. This drawing shows a twig with finely toothed, ovate leaves and blossoms arranged in small clusters. Each flower consists of four ivory-coloured petals alternating with dark stamens. The ovary can be seen at the centre of the corolla and ends in a long stylus.

The bark, leaves and seeds of the spindle-tree contain a compound that acts as a stimulant to the heart and digestive system, and compresses were used to treat scabies. The seeds also contain a toxic alkaloid, and Theophrastus called it ευώνυμος *(euonimos)* in his 'Περί Φυτών Ιστορίας' (*Historia plantarum*), in reference to the danger that it presented; while ευώνυμος means literally 'of good (i.e. auspicious) name', it was also a euphemism for a bad omen. The Italian name *berretto del prete* ('priest's beret') and the Flemish *kardinaalsmats* ('cardinal's mitre') were inspired by the form of the fruit.

187. Willow, *Salix* sp.

Erbario Miniato, fol. 187 (RL 27877)

Watermark: Fleur de lys 47

NUMBERING: *683*

ANNOTATION: [cut; *Vetreca* ('osier') in the index]

The willows, of the genus *Salix*, belong to the family Salicaceae and include about 300 species, mostly found in the temperate and cold regions of the northern hemisphere, where they flourish in damp and alluvial sites. This drawing shows a branch of a willow (the exact species cannot be identified), erect and bearing long, narrow, dark green leaves with lighter undersides. At its apex is a curious malformation, thickly covered with short, apparently trilobed leaves and probably caused by a virus.

188. Stock, *Matthiola* sp.; Hoary stock, *Matthiola incana* (L.) R. Br.

Erbario Miniato, fol. 188 (RL 27878)

Watermark: Fleur de lys 45

NUMBERING: *684*

ANNOTATION: *Viola gialla pulianta* ('Many-flowered yellow violet')

VERSO: Bulb of a large-fruited grape hyacinth, *Muscarimia macrocarpa* (Sweet) Garbari, with annotation: *Radice de Jacinto butroide / overo Muschio Greco* ('Root of the grape hyacinth or Greek musk')

The recto of this folio shows two plants. On the left is a thick, tapering stem, with narrow, elliptical leaves, terminating in six flowers carried on long, slender peduncles. Each flower has an elongated green calyx composed of narrow sepals with pointed apices and a large number of yellow petals. From the centres of two flowers spring two other flowers, the sort of curiosity beloved of Renaissance horticulturists. The species cannot be identified with certainty, though it is possibly a garden form of stock.

On the right is the hoary stock (see also **191** and **192**), another member of the Brassicaceae family, which grows in southern Europe, Cyprus and Algeria, on seaside cliffs and old walls at altitudes from sea level to 600m; it has also become naturalized elsewhere and is widely cultivated as a garden plant. The specimen has a slender branching stem and pale red flowers made up of four petals with long peduncles and elongated calyxes. The stamens and pistils cannot be seen, and the leaves of the plant are not shown, though on one of the lower branches an immature fruit can be seen.

These plants were formerly included in the genus *Cheiranthus*, but in 1812 the English botanist Robert Brown placed them in a new genus, *Matthiola*, in honour of Mattioli. *Cheiranthus* came from the Greek χείρ (*cheir*), 'hand', and ἄνθος (*anthos*), 'flower', referring to the bouquets of hoary stocks that were carried during religious festivals.

On the verso of the folio is a drawing of the bulb of a grape hyacinth, probably *Muscarimia macrocarpa*, with the form and colour of the tunics and rootlets well shown. The entire plant is illustrated in **198**, where this drawing of the bulb is copied.

verso

188.
6114
Viola gialla pulianta

189. Marvel of Peru, *Mirabilis jalapa* L.

Erbario Miniato, fol. 189 (RL 27879)

NUMBERING: *685*

ANNOTATION: *Viola Peruviana. nel eicones. 315* ('Peruvian violet. In the *Eicones*, 315').
[From Tabernaemontanus 1590, p. 315]

The marvel of Peru, of the family Nyctaginaceae, was imported to Europe from the mountains of Peru during the first half of the sixteenth century. It was soon being cultivated all over the continent, as is reflected in many botanical illustrations of the period – in Tabernaemontanus's *Eicones plantarum* cited here, for example, or the drawing by Jacopo Ligozzi in the Uffizi (1940 Orn., of *c.* 1577–87). Its popularity was due to its variety of colours, which appear as stripes on the flowers, not depicted here. It was named *Admirabilis peruana* (e.g. Clusius 1601, p. lxxxviii); Gerard (1597, p. 272) described it as 'rather the Marvell of the World, than of Peru alone', but its status as a garden plant waned after the eighteenth century. Clusius had remarked that the plant was sometimes classified as an *Ipomoea*, and the specific epithet comes from a confusion with the jalap, *Ipomoea purga*, a Mexican species (one of the common names of *Mirabilis jalapa* is false jalap).

The stem of the specimen is erect, branching and smooth. Its leaves are ovate with short petioles and slightly toothed margins. The flowers are deep red with a long funnel-shaped corolla terminating in five broad lobes; the stamen and pistils cannot be seen.

189.
605
Viola Peruviana . nel Icones. 315

190. Sweet rocket, *Hesperis matronalis* L.

Erbario Miniato, fol. 190 (RL 27880)

Watermark: Eagle 15

NUMBERING: *686*

ANNOTATION: *Viola hyemalis flore albo.; Viola hyemalis pupurea; nel Eicones Plantarum, 308* ('White flowered winter violet; purple winter violet. In the *Eicones Plantarum*, 308'). [From Tabernaemontanus 1590, p. 308]

This drawing shows two stems of the sweet rocket or dame's violet, a perennial of the family Brassicaceae that is common in southern and central Europe (and naturalized in the rest of the world), growing in damp forests and ravines to an altitude of 1,200m. According to Clusius, the sweet rocket was brought from Turkey to western Europe, where it was first cultivated in the gardens of Austria. It became popular as a house plant during the first half of the eighteenth century and many cultivars were developed, but the plant later faded from fashion. The *Erbario* inscriptions are taken from Tabernaemontanus's *Eicones plantarum* of 1590 (see Fig. 9, p. 28).

The stem on the left is erect, thick and smooth, while that on the right is covered with erect hairs. The alternate, lanceolate leaves have either very short or absent petioles, finely toothed margins and acute apices. In the specimen on the right the leaves too are covered with downy hairs. Branches carrying the plant's flowers and fruit grow from the axils of the leaves. The flowers, arranged in clusters of up to five blossoms, have light-coloured calyxes and corollas composed of four white petals with rounded apices; in the specimen on the right the petals are veined with pink. The fruit (siliqua) consists of long, slender, conspicuously knobbed pods.

190.

606

Viola Hyemalis Flore albo. Viola Hyemalis purpurea

nel Icones Plantarum, 308

191. Hoary stock, *Matthiola incana* (L.) R. Br.

Erbario Miniato, fol. 191 (RL 27881)

NUMBERING: *687*

ANNOTATION: [cut] *Viola* [*doppia*] ('Double violet')

This work illustrates a many-petalled, cultivated variety of the hoary stock (see **188**). The thick, erect stem of the plant terminates in a flower, while three other flowers and one closed bud grow on long, erect peduncles from the axils of the leaves. The flowers have deeply toothed calyxes and corollas made up of many bright red petals.

192. Hoary stock, *Matthiola incana* (L.) R. Br.

Erbario Miniato, fol. 192 (RL 27882)

Watermark: Fleur de lys 34

NUMBERING: *688*

This drawing shows an entire plant of the hoary stock (see **188**), with a long, smooth taproot. The thick, erect stem bears a large number of linear leaves that broaden gradually and end in rounded apices, some of which are wilting. The upper part of the plant bears numerous dark purple flowers made up of four petals with elongated calyxes and long peduncles; the pistils and stamens are not visible. The drawing appears to be in a different hand from the majority of the *Erbario* studies.

193. Pot marigold, *Calendula officinalis* L. cv.

Erbario Miniato, fol. 193 (RL 27883)

NUMBERING: *689*

ANNOTATION: *CALENDOLA PROLIFERA . II* ('Prolific marigold. Second type')

The artist shows here the curious bloom of a cultivated variety of the pot marigold (see **149** and cf. **151**). The erect stem with its long, dark green leaves culminates in a large orange flower head from whose base spring ten smaller flower heads of the same colour borne on slender peduncles. The central capitulum is made up of a small number of tubular flowers surrounded by concentric circles of ligulate flowers, while the smaller capitulums arranged in a circle around the central cluster are composed of tubular flowers surrounded by a single row of ligulate flowers. This type of *mostruosità* was particularly prized by botanists and collectors of the period. The name used for the plant in the annotation, *Calendola Prolifera II*, was probably drawn from Besler's *Hortus Eystettensis* of 1613, where the pot marigold is illustrated with the same name.

191.

CALENDOLA PROLIFERA.II

194. Rattle, *Rhinanthus* sp.

Erbario Miniato, fol. 194 (RL 27884)

The specimen on the right cut from another sheet and pasted on to the folio

NUMBERING: *690*

ANNOTATION: [cut; *Cresta di Gallo* ('cockscomb') in the index]

This drawing shows, over life-size, three inflorescences of some species of the rattle (*Rhinanthus* sp.), of the family Scrophulariaceae. The genus is spread diffusely in the mountainous zones of the northern hemisphere, where it grows in pastures and grasslands. It is not possible to identify the species because the main body of the plant is not shown, and furthermore each species exhibits a marked seasonal polymorphism.

From the apex of a slender stem springs the rattle's curious inflorescence, which is formed of many flowers, each of them with a large calyx covered with a dark green, finely toothed bract; the head is subtended by four to six long ovate or linear bracts that are either smooth or dentate at their base. The plant's tiny pink bilabial flower can be seen at the apex. The term *Rhinanthus* derives from the Greek ρίς (*rhis*), 'nose', and ανθός (*anthos*), 'flower', a reference to the upper lip of the flower's corolla, which resembles a nose. The index to the volume calls the plant a 'cresta di gallo', suggesting that the specimen might be the yellow-rattle, *Rhinanthus crista-galli*.

194.
690

195. Jerusalem artichoke, *Helianthus tuberosus* L.

Erbario Miniato, fol. 195 (RL 27885)

Watermark: Bird 19

NUMBERING: *691*

ANNOTATION: *Dal Volgo tartufoni bian*[*chi*]; *Helitropio de India* ('Commonly called white truffles; Indian heliotrope')

The annotation 'Helitropio de India' would suggest this is a Jerusalem artichoke (see **206**), here showing the basal part with two opposite leaves and five tubers growing in the midst of finely branching roots. The Jerusalem artichoke is sometimes called *tartufo di canna* ('cane truffle') in Italy, comparable to the name 'tartufoni bianchi' in the annotation.

195.
Dal Vesgo. Tartufani bian
Helitropio de India

196. Sunflower, *Helianthus annuus* L.

Erbario Miniato, fol. 196 (RL 27886)

Watermark: Eagle 15

NUMBERING: *692*

ANNOTATION: *Pianta Massima, Sole Indiano / Corona Regale. Coppa di Giove / Belide Pliniano. Tromba de Amore / Rosa de Hierico. Solsequia. Eliotropia, / Veneratrice del Sole. / Faorisce venere grandemente à chi il mangia. / la gomma che nasce nel suo tronco, abrusiata* [...] ('Large plant; Indian sun; royal crown; Jupiter's cup; Pliny's *Belide*; trumpet of love; rose of Jericho; *Solsequia*; heliotrope; venerator of the sun. The libido of those who eat it is greatly enhanced. The latex produced in its stem, when burned ...')

The sunflower is an annual of the family Asteraceae. Originally from the Americas, it is now cultivated all over the world. The stem is smooth and thick and bears several alternate leaves on long sturdy stems. Since the page has been trimmed none of the leaves are complete but they appear to be heart-shaped with entire margins. At the apex of the stem hangs a single head made up of a large disc of tubular flowers; at its centre a ring of darker flowers surrounds a central mass of flowers that are still in the early stages of anthesis. An outer corona of ligulate flowers completes the flower head. The seed receptacle is covered with large, scale-like bracts.

The Incas believed their king was descended from the Sun God, and adopted the sunflower as a symbol of sovereignty. Seeds of the sunflower were presented to Philip II of Spain by Hernando Pizarro (the brother of Francisco Pizarro), and the plant was soon popular in Europe, as the multiplicity of names given here suggests. It was frequently illustrated, among the most notable examples in print being the engraving in Besler's *Hortus Eystettensis* (1613, II, pl. 1). Ulisse Aldrovandi owned two drawings of a sunflower (Bologna, BU, MS Aldrovandi, *Tavole* vol. 1, *Piante*, fols 76–77), and Daniel Froeschl showed both front and back views of the flower in the *Codice Casabona* (Pisa, BU, MS 513bis, *c.* 1580–90).

196.
692
Pianta Massima, Sole Indiano.
Corona Regale, Coppa di Gioue
Belide Pliniano, Tromba de Amore
Rosa di Hierico, Solsequia Eliotropia,
Veneratrice del Sole.
uenere grandemente à chi il mangia.
la gomma che nasce nel suo tronco. abruciata

197. Nutmeg grape hyacinth, *Muscari muscarimi* Medik. 1791

Erbario Miniato, fol. 197 (RL 27887)

Watermark: Letter 19

ANNOTATION: *HYACINTHUS BOTRYOIDES CALCEDONICUS MUSCHATUS*

The nutmeg grape hyacinth is a perennial of the family Hyacinthaceae, introduced into Europe from Turkey (hence 'Calcedonicus') in the sixteenth century as an ornamental garden plant. This drawing shows the entire plant except for its bulb. The seven long leaves are linear in form and bent into a V along the central vein; their upper surfaces are lighter in colour than their undersides. The scape is sturdy and sinuous and bears a raceme of flowers growing on short peduncles. The perianth is vase-shaped, either yellow or pink in colour depending on the maturity of the flower, and tipped with violet at the opening of the throat.

197.

HYACINTHVS BOTRYOIDES CALCEDONICVS MVSCHATVS

198. Large-fruited grape hyacinth, *Muscarimia macrocarpa* (Sweet) Garbari

Erbario Miniato, fol. 198 (RL 27888)

NUMBERING: *693*

ANNOTATION: [cut] *Hyacinthus botryoides* ~~*Cal*~~ *Chalcedonicus* [–]*x muscatus*

This drawing portrays the flowering stem of another species of grape hyacinth (see **197**) together with a detail of its bulb enclosed in a whitish tunic. The somewhat casually drawn bulb appears to be copied from the illustration on the verso of **188**.

Originally from Turkey and the Cyclades, this flower is now cultivated in gardens and naturalized in various parts of Italy, particularly the Marches and Sicily. The five linear leaves of the plant are folded into a V along the central axis and the thick, straight scape bears a raceme of yellow, urn-shaped flowers. Jacopo Ligozzi painted a fine picture of this plant, today in the Uffizi (1903 Orn., *c.* 1577–87).

198
693
Hyacinthus botryoides
+muscatus.

199. Crown imperial, *Fritillaria imperialis* L.

Erbario Miniato, fol. 199 (RL 27889)

Flower and stalk cut from another sheet and pasted over an earlier drawing

Watermark: Fleur de lys 55

NUMBERING: *694*

ANNOTATION: *quando tre. e' quando / quattro fiore; Corona imperatoria venuta de gostantinopole, la virtu / de la quale participa del Giglio e' la scrive il Dodoneo* ('Sometimes three, sometimes four flowers; crown imperial which shares its properties with the lily, brought from Constantinople and written about by Dodoens'). [From Dodoens 1583, p. 202]

The crown imperial is a perennial bulbous species of the family Liliaceae, native to Pakistan and the temperate zones of Asia (see also **200**). The plant was introduced into Europe in the 1570s under the name 'Persian lily' (see **207**), and soon became a showpiece in many gardens. It is described and illustrated in the most important treatises and florilegia of the sixteenth and seventeenth centuries (e.g. Fig. 16, p. 40), including Dodoens's *Pemptades*, cited here (Fig. 10, p. 29). The crown imperial was adopted as the symbol of the Giardino dei Semplici of Pisa, the first botanical garden to be established in Europe (in 1543/4), and an image of the flower was carved in bas relief on one of the original doors to the garden, today conserved in its museum.

From the thick stem grow a large number of dark green, linear leaves. The scape, which is also quite thick, carries at its end a single flower; a pencil outline indicates a second, but the upper portion of the plant has been drawn on a separate trapezoidal piece of paper, pasted for some reason over an earlier version of the plant that showed at least three flowers. The flower hangs from a reflexed peduncle with a tuft of long, leaf-like bracts radiating above it. The corolla is composed of six orange-red tepals, with long stamens bearing yellow anthers at their extremities.

199
694
quando tre è quando
quattro fiore
Corona imperatoria venuta de gostantinopole. La virtu
de la quale participa del Giglio è la scrive il Dodoneo.

200. Crown imperial, *Fritillaria imperialis* L.

Erbario Miniato, fol. 200 (RL 27890)

Watermark: Fleur de lys 48

NUMBERING: *695*

ANNOTATION: *CORONA IMPERIALE* ('Crown imperial')

This drawing shows another flowering stem of the crown imperial (see **199**). The plant's thick, smooth stem carries ten long, dark green leaves, lanceolate with a projecting ridge that gives them their characteristic keel shape. The scape is erect and carries at its apex a large tuft of leaf-like bracts and three bright red flowers that hang from reflexed peduncles; yellow stamens can be seen protruding from their corollas.

CORONA IMPERIALE

201. Foxglove, *Digitalis purpurea* L.

Erbario Miniato, fol. 201 (RL 27891)

Cut from another sheet (405 x 258 mm) and inlaid; the title at bottom and the left-hand specimen also cut from other sheets and respectively pasted on to the folio and inlaid

ANNOTATION: *DIGITALE; DIGITALIS / PURPUREA* ('Foxglove; purple foxglove')

LITERATURE: Blunt/Raphael 1979, p. 105, pl. 105

The foxglove is a perennial of the family Scrophulariaceae that now grows throughout Europe, preferring siliceous soil, at altitudes from sea level to 1,700m. It was not described by the writers of antiquity and may have been introduced to southern Europe in the sixteenth century. The first naturalist to describe the plant was Leonhart Fuchs, who called it 'digitalis' in his work *De historia stirpium* (1542).

The specimen on the right has a smooth, flexible, tapering stem and lanceolate leaves with toothed margins and dark green veins that stand out against the lighter green of the leaf blade. At the apex is a dense raceme of bell-shaped flowers, all shown growing in the same direction. The flowers have short peduncles, linear bracts and short, deeply toothed calyxes. The corolla is dark pink in colour; its throat is dotted with numerous white spots, each of which contains a tiny black dot at its centre. The first two blossoms are shown as already fallen, exposing the flower's calyx and forked stigma, while the uppermost blooms are still in the bud. The stem on the left is similar, but light brown rather than green in colour, with younger flowers and a larger proportion of buds. The lower part of the plant and its root system are not shown.

Up until 1775, when its heart-stimulating properties were discovered by William Withering, the foxglove was considered merely a source of laxative, emetic and wound-healing remedies. The active substances digitalin and digitoxin are contained in the basal rosette of leaves.

201
DIGITALE
DIGITALIS
PVRPVREA

202. Chimney bellflower, *Campanula pyramidalis* L.

Erbario Miniato, fol. 202 (RL 27892)

Watermark: Fleur de lys 57

NUMBERING: *697*

ANNOTATION: *Piramidale campanula* ('pyramidal bellflower')

VERSO: offset of **171**

The chimney bellflower is a perennial of the family Campanulaceae, native to the mountains of the Balkans. The slender stem of this specimen ends in a raceme of bell-shaped flowers. The leaf is ovate with a pointed apex and undulating margins, carried on a stem that is as long as the leaf blade. At the axil of the leaf four small bracts arranged in a verticil can be seen. The flowers grow from the ends of long, slender, slightly reflexed peduncles; their corollas are pale blue and terminate in five lobes whose pointed ends curve backwards, as do the five linear teeth of their calyxes. A long, curving yellow stylus emerges from the throat of each flower.

The plant owes its English name to its decorative use in fireplaces during the summer, a custom also found in France.

202.
697
Piramidale campanula

203. Jerusalem cross or Maltese cross, *Lychnis chalcedonica* L.

Erbario Miniato, fol. 203 (RL 27893)

Watermark: Eagle 15

NUMBERING: *698*

ANNOTATION: *Flos Constantinopolitanus. / dal Dononeo; ditto da alcuni Scarlatino* ('Flower of Constantinople, in Dodoens; called by some *Scarlatino*'). [From Dodoens 1583, p. 178]

VERSO: offsets of **206** and **211**

The Jerusalem cross or Maltese cross is a herbaceous perennial of the family Caryophyllaceae, native to western Russia and temperate zones of Central Asia and now cultivated all over the world (see also **204**). The stem is erect, slender and covered with downy hairs. It carries three pairs of opposite leaves, sessile and lanceolate with undulating margins. The stem terminates in a corymb of bright red flowers growing from long green calyxes. The corolla is composed of five deeply indented petals; the pistils and stamens cannot be seen.

The name *Lychnis* was first used by Theophrastus and may have come from the Greek for lamp, λύχνος (*lychnos*), since the cottony down that covers the leaves was used to make wicks for oil lamps. The plant was treated as a novelty in the sixteenth century, and its origin attributed to its introduction from Constantinople (the specific epithet comes from the ancient name of the area, Chalcedon). It became a favourite garden plant and remains so to this day. In addition to the scarlet variety shown here, pink and white varieties also exist.

203.
690
Flos Constantinopolitanus.
dal Dononeo
ditto da alcuni Scarlatino

204. Jerusalem cross or Maltese cross, *Lychnis chalcedonica* L.

Erbario Miniato, fol. 204 (RL 27894)

NUMBERING: *699*

ANNOTATION: *FLOS CONSTANTINOPOLITANUS* ('Flower of Constantinople')

Like the preceding folio, this shows a Jerusalem cross or Maltese cross in full flower. Its erect, slender stem is covered with downy hairs. The two pairs of opposite leaves are lanceolate with undulating margins. The stem terminates in a dense corymb of flowers with long narrow calyxes and bright red corollas, each made up of five deeply indented petals.

204
FLOS CONSTANTINOPOLITANVS
669

205. Snake's-head fritillary, *Fritillaria meleagris* L.

Erbario Miniato, fol. 205 (RL 27895)

NUMBERING: *700*

ANNOTATION: [cut] *Meleagrede da Altri fritte*[*llaria*] ('*Meleagrede*, called fritillary by others')

VERSO: offset of **172**

The snake's-head fritillary belongs to the family Liliaceae. Native to western Europe, it is now common as far south as the mountainous regions of Italy, growing in pastures and grassy terrain below the tree line. The stem of the plant is erect, smooth and sinuous with alternate, long, narrow leaves. It terminates in a cluster of leaf-like bracts and three flowers that hang from long peduncles. Each corolla is made up of six dark pink petals spotted with ivory and purple. The artist shows three other specimens with lighter coloured flowers; at lower left the stamens and pistils can also be glimpsed. The fruit, shown whole and in cross-section at upper left, takes the form of a capsule made up of three erect lobes with bracts growing some way down the peduncle. The light-coloured seeds are oval in shape and come to a point at one end. The bulb is squat and rounded in form with a yellowish-white tunic.

The genus *Fritillaria* comprises about fifty different species (see also **199–200**, **207**, **211**), all native to the northern hemisphere and prized for their decorative flowers. The name was coined in the sixteenth century by Lobelius (Matthias de l'Obel) from the Latin *fritillus*, dice box, a reference to the chequered pattern of purple and white that decorates the tepals. The epithet *meleagris* was assigned by Dodoens, based on the Greek μελεαγρίς (*meleagris*), a guinea fowl, whose feathers bear similar markings.

205.
700
Meleagride da Altri fritte

206. Jerusalem artichoke, *Helianthus tuberosus* L.

Erbario Miniato, fol. 206 (RL 27896)

NUMBERING: *701*

ANNOTATION: *Elitropio dindia* ('Indian heliotrope')

The Jerusalem artichoke is a perennial of the family Asteraceae (see also **195**). Native to North America, it was introduced to Europe during the sixteenth century, and in many regions of Italy it may now be found growing spontaneously, particularly along water courses, at altitudes from sea level to 800m. The plant was introduced to England in 1617 from the celebrated Farnese garden in Rome, where it had been cultivated for some time. The Italians called the plant *girasole articiocco* ('artichoke sunflower'), because the tuber tastes like the globe artichoke. The theory that 'Jerusalem' is derived from 'girasole' was first circulated by Sir James Edward Smith, but there is an alternative explanation: Salaman (1940) suggested that it was derived from Ter Neusen, a Dutch supply centre for the vegetable.

Unusually, the illustration is orientated longitudinally. The stem on the right is light brown and bears alternate leaves, ovate in shape with toothed margins and pointed tips. Small branches ending in flower buds (and a flower outlined in pencil) grow from the apices of the leaves. The flowers are drawn separately in more detail, growing from erect and slender peduncles, each made up of a central core of tightly bunched tubular flowers surrounded by long, ligulate phyllarries. In the drawing at centre the seed receptacle with its scaly involucre can be clearly seen.

206.
Chitropis lindia

207. Persian fritillary, *Fritillaria persica* L.

Erbario Miniato, fol. 207 (RL 27897)

NUMBERING: *702*

ANNOTATION: *Giglio Persiano;* [cut: *Radica del la / C* [*orona*] *Imperiale*] ('Persian lily; [root of the crown imperial]')

The Persian fritillary is a perennial belonging to the family Liliaceae that originally came from western Asia and was introduced to Europe as an ornamental plant at the end of the sixteenth century. The stem is erect, smooth and tapering and the leaves elongated and lanceolate. The flowers, arranged in a loose raceme, hang from reflexed peduncles with a long linear bract growing from the axil of each. The dark pink tepals are faintly spotted with purple.

To the left is a large drawing of a bulb; the cancelled annotation at lower right indicates it to be the bulb of the crown imperial (see **199–200**), though the index to the volume entitles the whole sheet 'cipolla di Giglio Persiano', implying that the bulb is that of the fritillary.

207.
302
Giglio Persiano
Radisa de la

208. Tulip, *Tulipa* sp.

Erbario Miniato, fol. 208 (RL 27898)

Watermark: Fleur de lys 17

NUMBERING: *703*

ANNOTATION: [cut] *Tulipa*[*ni*]

The tulip is a flower belonging to the vast family of Liliaceae. Given the complexity of the genus *Tulipa* and the innumerable cultivated forms that have been developed since antiquity, it is not possible to identify with any precision the flowers shown here, though they could represent specimens of either *T. cretica* or *T. saxatilis*.

The stem of the flower on the right is erect and smooth with a long, linear, sheath-like leaf enveloping its lower part, while higher up are a pair of shorter leaves. The stem terminates in a flower bud composed of six narrow, elliptical tepals. The three outer tepals (as can be seen in the detail at lower right) are red in colour with a wide band of white along each margin, while the three inner tepals are completely white with a splash of red at their base. The flower has six bluish-grey stamens. The ovary and stylus are light green and shorter than the stamens.

208

209. Wild tulip, *Tulipa sylvestris* L. cv.

Erbario Miniato, fol. 209 (RL 27899)

NUMBERING: *704*

ANNOTATION: *TULIPANE II* ('Tulip, second type')

This drawing illustrates the so-called wild tulip, with a second flower drawn on the right. The scape is erect with long, linear, carinate leaves growing from its base. The single yellow flower is made up of eight petals, an unusual occurrence since tulips normally have six petals, as is shown in the drawing on the right. The eight-petal tulip is therefore probably a cultivar, as ornamental cultivars are normally selected to yield larger flowers with more petals. The internal petals of the flower are broadly obovate while the external petals are narrower and almost lance-shaped, with faint green veins in their central zone.

210. Unidentified bulbous plant

Erbario Miniato, fol. 210 (RL 27900)

NUMBERING: *705*

ANNOTATION: *Unifolio*; ~~*Monofillo*~~ ('Single-leaf')

This drawing shows a bulb with a single leaf growing from a long, slender petiole. The leaf, which is long and elliptical in form, has entire margins and an acute apex. The bulb is pear-shaped with a white tunic that does not continue along the leaf's petiole. Too few details are provided to allow an identification of the species or genus of this plant, although it may perhaps belong to the lily family.

211. Fritillary, *Fritillaria* sp.

Erbario Miniato, fol. 211 (RL 27901)

ANNOTATION: *MELEAGREDE DA ALTRI FRITTELARIA* ('*Meleagrede*, called by others fritillary')

The stem of this fritillary (see **205**, **207**) is erect, smooth and sinuous. The leaves are slightly carinate, and linear in form with entire margins and acute apices. The flower, made up of six dark pink tepals with purple veins, hangs from a long reflexed peduncle with three leafy bracts growing from its axil. The stamens and pistils cannot be seen, and the bulb is not shown. The species cannot be identified with certainty, although it could be *F. orientalis*.

TVLIPANE II.
704
209

705
210
Unifolio·
Monofillo

MELEAGREDE DA ALTRI FRITTELARIA
211

LOOSE DRAWINGS FROM A COMPANION VOLUME TO THE *ERBARIO MINIATO*: 212–277

As discussed on p. 36, there were originally two other companion volumes to the *Erbario Miniato*. The first is untraced and the drawings from the second, bearing 'Pozzo' numbers in the range *279* (*circa*) to *498*, were cut down and remounted in the eighteenth century. Most were sold from the Royal Library in the 1920s and sixty-seven have since been identified (**212–277**). The surviving 'Pozzo' numbering on these sheets suggests that they were arranged, like the third volume – the *Erbario Miniato* itself (**1–211**) – in the order of Pietro Andrea Mattioli's *Discorsi* (the 1568 edition). They have thus been catalogued here in the order of the surviving 'Pozzo' numbering.

212. Soapwort, *Saponaria officinalis* L.

Present location unknown

288 x 262 mm. *Watermark*: Fleur de lys on hills, in circle, with surmounting letter M (type of Fleur de lys 44–55)

NUMBERING: *279*

ANNOTATION: [cut] *Gentiana minore; Gentiana volgarmente da / alcuni si chiama Cruciata. / e' da quegli de la valle Anania. / Pettimborsa; e' alcuni Saponaria* ('Lesser gentian, commonly called *Cruciata* by some, and *Pettimborsa* by those of the Anania valley; and by some *Saponaria*') [From Mattioli 1568, p. 683]

MOUNT SHEET: Type D

PROVENANCE: Boone sale, lot 136

The soapwort is a herbaceous perennial of the family Caryophyllaceae, found throughout Europe and the temperate regions of western Asia (and naturalized elsewhere) in damp, uncultivated or forested terrain from sea level to an altitude of 1,000m. In Italy it may be found growing spontaneously in broad riverbeds, particularly in forested areas, that are dry during the summer. The annotation cites the 'valle Anania', the ancient name for the Non Valley in southern Trentino, a region where Mattioli spent some time as a guest of the prince-bishop Bernardo Clesio.

The stem is erect, robust and slightly sinuous. The leaves are opposite, sessile and lance-shaped with entire margins and acute apices. Parallel veins can be seen running along the upper sides of the blades. The plant's flowers are arranged in a cyme at the apex of the stem and have corollas composed of five long, narrow pink petals, seen in a detail at upper right; the calyx is elongated, narrow and toothed. Neither the reproductive structures nor the root system are shown.

Every part of the soapwort contains saponin, a substance that lathers in water and emulsifies oils, resins and camphor. The dried leaves and roots, broken up, were used to clean wool and wash clothing. Preparations made from the plant were used as a sudorific, an anti-rheumatic and an anti-inflammatory for the respiratory passages, though the plant has a potentially hazardous haemolytic effect.

The annotation copies a passage from p. 683 of the *Discorsi*. The 'Gentiana minore' cited is illustrated on p. 681, which is a star or cross gentian, *Gentiana cruciata*, and not a soapwort.

Gentiana minore
279
Gentiana. volgarmente da
alcuni si chiama Cruciata.
e da quelli dela valle Anania.
Pettimborsa: e alcuni Saponaria.

213. Birthwort, *Aristolochia clematitis* L.

Present location unknown

375 x 257 mm

NUMBERING: *282*

ANNOTATION: *Aristolochia lunga a' la / medesima faculta de la / ritonda, 685.* ('Long *Aristolochia* has the same properties as the round one, 685.') [From Mattioli 1568, p. 685]

MOUNT SHEET: Type D

The birthwort is a herbaceous perennial of the family Aristolochiaceae which may be found throughout Europe and Asia Minor in broadleaved forests, hedges and uncultivated terrain with high levels of nitrogen, at altitudes from sea level to 1,000m. Almost all species of the genus *Aristolochia* have flowers that emit a putrid odour to attract pollinating insects.

The stem is erect and smooth, and bears at each node a leaf on a long petiole. The leaves are heart-shaped with acute apices, entire margins and conspicuous veins. At the axil of each leaf are three to four yellow flowers on slightly reflexed or erect peduncles. The corolla of the flower is composed of an elongated spathe, swollen at its base, indicating the presence of the ovary. The root at lower left is covered with brown bark, twisting, knobbed and sparsely branched. The fruit at lower right is a smooth green berry with fine, white, longitudinal striations and a curved pedicel; it is accompanied by an unfinished sketch of another fruit shown in cross-section. The 'round' Aristolochia referred to in the annotation (as sharing the same properties as this 'long' one) refers to snakeroot, *Aristolochia rotunda*, which Mattioli illustrated on p. 684 of the *Discorsi*.

The birthwort was known to the ancient Greeks and Romans, its name apparently deriving from the Greek ἄριστος (*aristos*), 'best', and λοχεία (*lochia*), 'childbirth'. Hippocrates believed that it could be used to treat infections of the womb. This application was revived later by herbalists applying the doctrine of signatures, since the form of the flower supposedly resembles a uterus. An infusion of the root was used to induce menstruation and abortions, but the plant contains a potent alkaloid which can lead to vomiting, enteritis and cardiac and respiratory paralysis.

Aristolochia lunga. a'la
medesima facultà dela
ritonda. 685.
282

214. Liquorice, *Glycyrrhiza glabra* L.

Private collection

268 x 260 mm

NUMBERING: *283*

MOUNT SHEET: trace of Type D at edges, laid on to modern mount with imitation Type D wash borders

Liquorice is a herbaceous perennial of the family Fabaceae, common in southern and western Europe and western Asia in arid terrain at altitudes from sea level to 1,000m. Since antiquity the liquorice has been prized for its root, which contains a sweet juice used to flavour sweets, pastries and liqueurs; the name *Glycyrrhiza* means 'sweet root'. Theophrastus referred to it as the 'Syrian root', suggesting that it had reached Greece from the Near East. The cultivated plant was brought to Italy from Spain by Benedictine monks during the tenth century.

The stem is erect and smooth, and bears four compound leaves, each made up of eight to ten ovate leaflets that have short petioles, entire margins and acute apices. The woody rhizome is knobby, twisted and branching, with a large number of long, slender rootlets growing from its nodes. The bark of the root is brown, while its wood is light yellow in colour. In the lower left is a detail showing a stem bearing flowers arranged in a dense raceme. Each flower has a long, narrow calyx carried on a short peduncle and pale pink petals. The reproductive structures are not shown.

A liquorice is illustrated on p. 688 of the *Discorsi*, after the 'Aristolochia lunga' on p. 685 (**213**) and before the 'Centaurea maggiore' on p. 690 (**215**).

283

215. Great knapweed, *Centaurea centaurium* L.

Collection of Patti Skouras, USA

496 x 271 mm

NUMBERING: *284*

ANNOTATION: *Centaurea / magiore.* 690 ('Greater centaury. 690') [From Mattioli 1568, p. 690]

MOUNT SHEET: Type D

PROVENANCE: Boone sale, lot 132

The great knapweed is a species of the family Asteraceae, native to southern Italy where it grows in broadleaved forests, especially of beech and oak, at altitudes between 500m and 1,500m (see also **216**). The drawing shows a dark green leaf blade deeply divided into eleven lanceolate lobes with acute apices and finely toothed margins. The lobes do not quite reach the central vein, which is lighter green in colour.

In Greek mythology, when the centaur Chiron was wounded by an arrow of Hercules poisoned with the blood of the Hydra, he treated the wound with the juice of a plant that has been identified as the great knapweed, hence its alternative names centaur's knapweed or centaury (see also **217**). The genus *Centaurea* includes a large number of species, the best known of which is the cornflower, *Centaurea cyanus*.

Centaurea
magiore. 690
284

216. Great knapweed, *Centaurea centaurium* L.

Private collection

306 x 256 mm

NUMBERING: *285*

ANNOTATION: *Centaurea magiore. fiorita.* *690* ('Greater centaury in flower. 690') [From Mattioli 1568, p. 690]

MOUNT SHEET: modern mount with imitation Type D wash borders

The drawing shows two flower heads of the great knapweed (see **215**). The stem is erect, slender and smooth and carries one branch. At the apex of the principal branch is a capitulum in full flower, consisting of an involucre of overlapping roundish scales with brown margins; the flowers have white, finely fringed corollas. The smaller branch bears a closed flower head.

Centaurea magiore · fiorita · 690
285

217. Common centaury, *Centaurium erythraea* Rafn

Windsor, RL 19387

277 x 230 mm

NUMBERING: *287*

ANNOTATION: [cut] *Unaltra Centaurea.* / [–] *del matiolo.*[–] ('Another centaury. Mattioli's [–]')

MOUNT SHEET: Type D

PROVENANCE: Sir Rex Nan Kivell

The common centaury is a herbaceous annual of the family Gentianaceae. It is widespread in Europe, North Africa and temperate zones of Asia as far east as Pakistan, growing in wet and sandy (even brackish) terrain, along shady paths and in open scrubland from sea level to an altitude of 1,500m. Like the great knapweed (**215–216**) the plant was associated with the myth of Hercules and the centaur Chiron; the genera *Centaurea* and *Centaurium* were often confused.

The stem is slender, erect and branching, with opposite, sessile, lanceolate leaves. The flowers are arranged in corymbs, some of which show further branching. The calyx, shown in a small detail to the left, is elongated with two subtended bracts. The corolla is pink in colour, tube-shaped and ends in five distinct lobes.

The specific epithet *erythraea* is derived from the Greek ερυθρός (*erythros*), 'red', from the colour of the flowers. Due to its antipyretic qualities it was called 'febbrifuga' (febrifuge), and it is found under this name in many medieval herbals. In southern Italy it was used to treat malaria long after the discovery of quinine, and an infusion of the plant is still used against fever in northern Scotland.

Cesi's annotation has been partially cut off, but probably cited the common centaury illustrated by Mattioli on p. 692 ('Centaurea minore').

Vnaltra Centaurea
287
del matiolo

218. Stemless carline thistle, *Carlina acaulis* L.

London, Victoria and Albert Museum, E.731-1949

252 x 246 mm

NUMBERING: *288*

ANNOTATION: *Chameleone Bianco, e' chiamato da Alcuni Carlin*[*a*]. ('White *Chameleone*, called by some *Carlina*.') [From Mattioli 1568, pp. 693–4]

MOUNT SHEET: Type D

PROVENANCE: Helen de Beer

The carline thistle is a herbaceous perennial of the family Asteraceae, common in fields in central and southern Europe at altitudes from sea level to 2,000m. The specimen bears five sessile, lanceolate leaves with deeply toothed and lobed margins. At the apex of the short stem is a large flower head whose involucre is composed of elongated yellow scales forming a false corolla around the capitulum. The plant ends in a straight taproot with three branches. The scales surrounding the flower head stand upright in dry weather and fold inwards when the weather becomes damp.

The name of the carline thistle is derived from Charlemagne, whose army was reputedly cured of plague by its use. The plant has sudorific, digestive or diuretic properties; its active principle is contained in the taproot and the rhizome, which in older plants divides into several branches. These have a flavour similar to that of the artichoke and in some countries are used as a herb.

Cameleone Bianco, è chiamato da Alcuni Carlin

219. Wild teasel, *Dipsacus fullonum* L.

Collection of Mark Storey, UK

377 x 260 mm

NUMBERING: *289*

ANNOTATION: *Dissaco, overo Labro di Veneré, e nelle / spetie de le piante spinose, la radice cotta / nel vino. e' poscia pesta'fino che venga a' modo / di cera. sana le fessure del sedere. é / le fistole. dicisi che i vermi che si ritrovano / ne le teste. legati in cuoio, e' attachati al collo o, / vero al braccio, sanano la febre quartana. 698* ('*Dissaco*, or lip of Venus. It belongs to the species of thorny plants. The root, cooked in wine and then ground until it becomes like wax, heals anal ruptures and fistulas. It is said that the worms that are found in the heads, wrapped in leather and attached to the neck or arm, cure quartan fever. 698') [From Mattioli 1568, pp. 697–8]

PROVENANCE: David Nash; Sotheby's (London), 5 July 2006, lot 95

The wild teasel is a herbaceous biennial of the family Dipsacaceae, common all over Europe, North Africa and the Near East in uncultivated and abandoned terrain at altitudes from sea level to 1,400m. The generic name *Dipsacus* derives from the Greek name for this plant, δίψακος (*dipsakos*), as found in Dioscorides and Galen, a reference to the cup-like form of the leaves that fill with water when it rains, from διψάω (*dipsao*), 'to be thirsty'. *Fullonum* comes from the Latin 'to full [i.e. cleanse and thicken] cloth', because the flower heads were used to comb or tease wool – hence the English name for the plant, teasel, and the Italian *cardo dei lanaioli*, 'woolworkers' thistle'. For centuries the plant was cultivated in areas where wool was produced.

The stem of this specimen is erect, thick and covered with spines. The leaves are lanceolate and deeply folded along their longitudinal axis, with entire margins and acute apices. They grow in opposite pairs that are united at their bases (connate). The central vein is covered with thick spines on the underside. Three branches spring from the last pair of leaves, each carrying an inflorescence subtended by four to six linear bracts covered with spines, and longer than the inflorescence itself. The flowers form a compact, oval head that appears to be spiny due to the many long, pointed scales that grow from the base of each flower. The lateral branches each bear a pair of connate leaves.

The 'Dissaco' illustrated by Mattioli on p. 698 of the *Discorsi*, cited here, is not the true teasel but *Dipsacus sativus*, which was also cultivated in antiquity for the same purpose but is now believed to be extinct in Italy. The true teasel appears on the next page as 'Un'altro Dissaco'. The name 'Labro di Venere' ('lip of Venus') cited in the annotation is a rendering of the old Latin name for the plant, *lavacrum Veneris*.

209
289
Dissaco, ouero Labro di Venere, è nelle
spetie de le piante spinose, la radice cotta
nel vino. è poscia pesta fino a modo
di cera. sana le fessure del sedere. e
le fistole. divisi che i uermi che si ritrouano
ne le teste. legati in cuoio, è attaccati al collo o,
uero al braccio, sanano la febre quintana. 698

220. Plymouth thistle, *Carduus pycnocephalus* L. 1762–3

Collection of Mia N. Weiner, USA

294 x 236 mm

NUMBERING: *290*

MOUNT SHEET: Type D

PROVENANCE: Phillips (London), 16 December 1992, lot 127

The Plymouth thistle is an annual or biennial species belonging to the family Asteraceae, common around the Mediterranean; it is also found in India and Pakistan, and is naturalized in Australia, New Zealand and parts of the United States. It is an invasive, adventitious plant that grows along roadsides and in pastures and other open, arid terrain.

This drawing shows the spiny-winged stem, branched at the apex. The leaves are alternate and sessile with deeply incised and toothed margins; at the apex of each tooth is a large spine. The stem ends in capitulums with involucres of acute spiny scales and light blue flowers.

220

221. Globe thistle, *Echinops sphaerocephalus* L.

Private collection

265 x 258 mm

NUMBERING: *292*

MOUNT SHEET: Type D

PROVENANCE: Boone sale, lot 135

LITERATURE: *Cassiano Segreti* 2000, cat. 91; *L'Uccelliera* 2000, fig. XVId, pp. 49, 116; *Cassiano Segreti* 2001, cat. 169

The globe thistle is a herbaceous perennial of the family Asteraceae, widespread in Europe and temperate regions of western Asia in uncultivated stony soil at low altitudes, though it will grow in almost any type of terrain and thrives best in light, calcareous, fairly fertile soil. It has been cultivated as a garden plant since the end of the sixteenth century.

The thick, tapering stem is covered with erect hairs. Its lobed, lanceolate leaves grow directly from the stem and envelop it at their distal ends; the margins are irregularly toothed, each tooth ending in a short spine. The lower sides of the leaves are covered with a thick layer of silky, silver-grey hairs. Branches growing from the axils of the leaves terminate, as does the main stem, in an inflorescence composed of numerous flowers, each surrounded by an involucre of spiny scales. The reproductive structures are not shown. The generic name *Echinops* refers to the hedgehog-like form of the inflorescence.

292

222. Globe artichoke, *Cynara scolymus* L.

Rome, Accademia Nazionale dei Lincei, Fondo A, 40bis

265 x 260 mm. *Watermark*: Star 4

NUMBERING: *293*

ANNOTATION: *Cardo. 705*. [From Mattioli 1568, p. 705]

MOUNT SHEET: Type D

PROVENANCE: Boone sale, lot 143; Margot Gordon, USA; Marcello Aldega, Italy

LITERATURE: *Cassiano Segreti* 2000, cat. 92; *L'Uccelliera* 2000, fig. xvb, pp. 48, 116; *Cassiano Segreti* 2001, cat. 170; Brevaglieri *et al*. 2007, fig. 31, p. 127

The globe artichoke is a scapose herbaceous annual of the family Asteraceae, widespread across the Mediterranean and now cultivated and naturalized all over the world (see also **223–226**, **284**, **293**). The artichoke was known to the Romans; Filippo Strozzi reintroduced the plant to Tuscany in the fifteenth century, having acquired seeds in the kingdom of Naples, whence its cultivation gradually spread across Europe. *Cynara scolymus* probably derives from the wild form *C. cardunculus*, which is common in central and southern Italy. The Italian name *carciofo* is derived from the Arabic *ḳaršūfa*; Mattioli noted that in Lombardy the plant was known as *archichiochi*. This sheet and **223–224** all refer to p. 705 of Mattioli's *Discorsi*, where the plant is illustrated as a 'cardo senza spine' ('thistle without thorns').

The drawing shows the fruiting part of an artichoke. Growing at the apex of a thick, smooth, erect stem is a capitulum formed of an involucre of overlapping, slightly reflexed scales arranged in rings. The flower head consists of a tuft of whitish bristles.

222

223. Globe artichoke, *Cynara scolymus* L.

Rome, Accademia Nazionale dei Lincei, Fondo A, 40bis

277 x 234 mm. *Watermark*: Eagle in circle with surmounting crown

NUMBERING: *295*

ANNOTATION: *Cardo.* <u>*705*</u> [From Mattioli 1568, p. 705]

MOUNT SHEET: Type D

PROVENANCE: Boone sale, lot 143; Margot Gordon, USA; Marcello Aldega, Italy

LITERATURE: *Cassiano Segreti* 2000, cat. 93; *L'Uccelliera* 2000, fig. xva, pp. 48, 116; *Cassiano Segreti* 2001, cat. 171; Brevaglieri *et al.* 2007, fig. 30, p. 127

Another globe artichoke is shown here (see **222**). The stem is thick, erect and ribbed. The involucre is composed of elongated, lanceolate scales with reflexed ends that are shallowly notched and terminate in a thick, slightly curved spine.

Cardo · 205

224. Globe artichoke, *Cynara scolymus* L.

Present location unknown

262 x 263 mm

NUMBERING: *296*

ANNOTATION: *Cardo. 705* [From Mattioli 1568, p. 705]

MOUNT SHEET: Type D

PROVENANCE: Kyburg Gallery, London

The stem of this globe artichoke (see **222**) is straight and thick with long, narrow leaves, loosely sketched. Both the stem and leaves are covered with fine, silky, white hairs. The stem terminates in a capitulum that is still enclosed within its involucre. The dark scales have notched apices and no spine.

225. Globe artichoke, *Cynara scolymus* L.

Collection of Patti Skouras, USA

338 x 260 mm

NUMBERING: *297*

ANNOTATION: *CARDO OVERO CARCIOFFO* ('*Cardo* or artichoke')

MOUNT SHEET: Type D

PROVENANCE: Boone sale, lot 145

In this specimen of a globe artichoke (see **222**) the stem is erect and slightly curved, with clearly marked ribs running along its length. The leaves are long, lanceolate and irregularly lobed with blunt apices. The floral involucre is composed of oval scales, green at the base and brownish-purple along the margins and apex, which ends in a small spine.

226. Globe artichoke, *Cynara scolymus* L.

Collection of Patti Skouras, USA

393 x 265 mm

NUMBERING: *298*

MOUNT SHEET: Type D

PROVENANCE: Boone sale, lot 145

This globe artichoke (see **222**) has a thick, erect, ribbed stem. The leaf is linear and sessile with deeply round-toothed margins. The involucre is globular and made up of oval scales with blunt apices ending in a thick yellow spine.

224

CARDO OVERO CARCIOFFO
297

226

227. Scotch or cotton thistle, *Onopordum acanthium* L.

Private collection

398 x 265 mm

NUMBERING: *299*

ANNOTATION: [cut] *ACANTHIO / la radice, overo le frondi / beute vaglino à quella spetie. / di spasimo che si dimanda* [M: *chiama*]. */ opisthotono. ~~686~~ 708* ('*Acanthio.* The root or leaves when drunk are useful against that sort of spasm that is called tetanic. ~~686~~ 708) [From Mattioli 1568, pp. 708–9]

MOUNT SHEET: Type D

PROVENANCE: Boone sale, lot 135

LITERATURE: *Cassiano Segreti* 2000, cat. 90; *L'Uccelliera* 2000, fig. XVIC, pp. 49, 116; *Cassiano Segreti* 2001, cat. 168

The Scotch or cotton thistle is a herbaceous biennial of the family Asteraceae, widespread in central and southern Europe and western Asia. It is a weed that grows on uncultivated terrain at altitudes of up to 1,500m. This thistle was cited by Pliny, who used its Greek name ονόπορδον (*onopordon*), from όνος (*onos*) 'ass', and πέρδομαι (*perdomai*), 'to break wind' – a description of what supposedly occurs after an ass eats the spiny plant. It was adopted as a heraldic device by the first kings of Scotland, following a legend that a Danish attack was thwarted when the Scots were awakened by the cries of a Danish soldier who had stepped on one. The flower became the national emblem of Scotland under James III (*r.* 1488–1513), who created the Order of the Thistle, the highest honour in Scotland (and in Britain second in precedence only to the Order of the Garter).

The stem is erect and completely hidden by its leaves, which are sessile and lanceolate with broadly toothed margins, many ending in a rigid spine. At the top of the stem are two flower heads enveloped in whorls of bracts made up of narrow scales, often ending in a spine. The flowers have pinkish corollas; their reproductive structures cannot be seen. The fleshy receptacle of the plant has a flavour similar to that of the artichoke. The seeds contain an oil that can be used for cooking or in lamps, and the dried plant was burned as fuel. The juice of the leaves was a traditional remedy for tumours.

ACANTHIO
la radice, ouero le frondi;
299

228. Rosemary, *Rosmarinus officinalis* L.

Windsor, RL 19388

219 x 262 mm. *Watermark*: Fleur de lys 55

NUMBERING: *311*

MOUNT SHEET: Type D

PROVENANCE: Sir Rex Nan Kivell

Rosemary is a perennial shrub belonging to the family Lamiaceae, native to the Mediterranean in open scrubland at altitudes from sea level to 900m, and now cultivated as a herb and decorative plant all over the world. The stem is robust and woody, and bears numerous long, narrow opposite leaves with a dark green central vein. At the tip of a small side branch there are flowers with light blue corollas. The body of the plant and its root system are not shown.

The name 'rosemary' comes from the Latin *ros marinus* ('sea dew'), referring to the colour of its flowers. Countless legends and traditions have sprung up around the reputed healing properties of the herb. For the ancient Egyptians the plant was a symbol of immortality, and a sprig of the herb was placed in the hand of the deceased to facilitate his journey to the next world. The Romans fashioned wreaths of rosemary to crown the statues of their household gods, the *lares*. During the Middle Ages objects made from rosemary wood were carried as talismans to ward off evil – it was believed, for example, that spoons made of the wood could prevent poisoning. Magical potions with rosemary as an ingredient are found down the centuries, such as an elixir of youth used by Queen Isabella of Hungary, or the 'vinegar of the four thieves', an anti-plague potion supposedly discovered by thieves in the course of a burglary, a legend recurring in several cities. Arab physicians were probably the first to extract essential oils from rosemary, the earliest credible reference to its distillation dating from the twelfth century.

228

229. Venice pea, *Lathyrus venetus* (Mill.) Wohlf.

Windsor, RL 19453

229 x 268 mm. *Watermark*: Eagle in circle with surmounting crown

NUMBERING: *315*

PROVENANCE: Eliette Bostrom

The Venice pea is a herbaceous perennial of the family Fabaceae, widespread in central, southern and eastern Europe in broadleaved forests at altitudes from sea level to 1,200m. The branch is slender and flexible, with pairs of lanceolate leaflets with entire margins and pointed tips. From the axils grow long branches terminating in racemes of dark pink flowers, which are succeeded by long, narrow pods, as shown on the lowest branch.

In antiquity the name λάθυρος (*lathyros*) was used for a variety of leguminous plants. Theophrastus used the word in his *Historia plantarum*, and a variant, λαθυρίς (*lathyris*), found in the texts of Dioscorides and Galen, gave rise to the Latin *lens* or lentil. Although many species in this genus are of great economic importance, *Lathyrus venetus* is of little interest to farmers or gardeners.

229

230. Winter savory, *Satureja montana* L.

Windsor, RL 19389

176 x 263 mm

NUMBERING: *320*

ANNOTATION: *Santoreggia, / domestica* ('Domestic *Santoreggia*')

MOUNT SHEET: Type D

PROVENANCE: Sir Rex Nan Kivell

The winter savory is a herbaceous perennial of the family Lamiaceae. It is common in Europe and temperate regions of Asia, where it grows in arid meadows with a calcareous or serpentine substrate at altitudes from sea level to 1,300m. The stem is slender and erect. The leaves are narrowly linear with entire margins and acute apices; the petiole is short or absent. At the apex of the stem are four fully opened flowers. At lower centre is a detail of a flower; the corolla is bilabial and light bluish-pink, with dark filaments and anthers protruding from the throat.

Winter savory was supposed to be an aphrodisiac; it was used in the orgiastic rites dedicated to the god Bacchus, and monks were prohibited from cultivating the plant. It was also thought to have magical properties, and that a sprig of the plant could keep away malign spirits, but Pliny warned that it should not be cut with an iron implement when gathered. In the Middle Ages, Saints Hildegaard and Albertus Magnus both prescribed savory for gout, paralysis, diarrhoea and amenorrhoea (Lazzeri 1996). The plant has antiseptic, antispasmodic and carminative properties, and was used as an expectorant, stimulant and stomachic. In Tuscany herbalists recommended a decoction of the plant for gastrointestinal colic, and savory was added to babies' bathwater to strengthen their legs.

230

231. Costmary or alecost, *Balsamita major* Desf.

Private collection

384 x 270 mm

NUMBERING: *323*

ANNOTATION: *Menta greca. 753.; Herba de S<u>a</u> Maria, dal Matthiolo Menta / greca, il succo di questa herba beuto amazza i, vermi / del corpo: giova alle frigidi-ta della madrice. Corrobora lo / stomacho tanto beuto, quanto impiastrato. di fuore, / e' ristagna gravimente i vomiti.* ('Greek mint, 753. Herb of Holy Mary, called by Mattioli Greek mint. The juice of this plant when drunk kills worms in the body. It is beneficial for infertility in women. It fortifies the stomach whether drunk or applied externally, and is effective in preventing further vomiting.') [From Mattioli 1568, pp. 753–4]

MOUNT SHEET: Type D

PROVENANCE: Boone sale, lot 139

LITERATURE: *Cassiano Segreti* 2000, cat. 88; *L'Uccelliera* 2000, fig. XVIA, pp. 49, 116; *Cassiano Segreti* 2001, cat. 166

The costmary or alecost is a herbaceous perennial of the family Asteraceae, native to Iran and Azerbaijan in damp undergrowth and along the banks of rivers, and now cultivated and naturalized all over the world, particularly in the Alps, China and India. The plant has been prized for its medicinal and aromatic properties since antiquity. The pharmacy of the monastery of Santa Maria Novella in Florence distilled the plant to obtain essential oils and other ingredients for products such as smelling salts (*acqua antisterica*), pungent lozenges (*pasticche di Santa Maria Novella*) and a skin tonic (*acqua di erba Santa Maria*).

The stem is erect, smooth and branching at its apex. The leaves are alternate and lanceolate with finely toothed margins, acute apices and short petioles. The flowers have yellow petals and stamens, and grow in clusters of four at the ends of the branches.

Menta greca. 153.
Herba de S.a Maria, dal Matthiolo Menta
greca, il succo di questa Herba bevuto amazza i uermi
del corpo: giova alle frigidita della madrice. Corrobora lo
stomacho tanto bevuto, quanto impiastrato. di fuore,
e ristagna gravimente i uomiti,
323

232. Nettle-leaved bellflower, *Campanula trachelium* L.

Windsor, RL 19390

259 x 246 mm

NUMBERING: *324*

MOUNT SHEET: Type D

PROVENANCE: Sir Rex Nan Kivell

The nettle-leaved bellflower is a herbaceous perennial of the family Campanulaceae. It is common in Europe and North Africa, and naturalized in North America, growing in sheltered spots at altitudes from sea level to 1,500m. The name *Campanula*, from the bell-like shape of the flower, was assigned to the genus by Dodoens in his treatise *Florum, et coronarium odoratumque . . . historia*, in 1569.

The stem is slender and flexible, with leaves and flowers growing from its nodes. The leaves are lanceolate with finely toothed margins and short petioles that are barely visible. The flower has a short, toothed calyx and a narrow tubular corolla, light blue faintly tinged with lilac and terminating in five or six narrow, pointed lobes. The yellow stigma can be seen at the mouth of the corolla.

324

233. Vetch, *Vicia* sp.

Windsor, RL 19454

303 x 262 mm. *Watermark*: Eagle in circle with surmounting crown

NUMBERING: *332*

PROVENANCE: Eliette Bostrom

This rather summary drawing illustrates the fruiting branch of a vetch (of the family Fabaceae), though it is not possible to identify the exact species. The erect stem is made up of straight internodes, each growing at a slight angle from the former. At the internodes are the plant's leaves, consisting of nine to eleven paired leaflets ending in a single terminal leaflet. The leaflets are elliptical in form with entire margins, and short petioles. From the axil of each leaf grows a branchlet carrying numerous knobbed pods (legumes) on short peduncles.

The name *Vicia* can be found in the works of Virgil. Some species of the genus are cultivated for food (such as the fava bean, *Vicia faba*) or as forage for animals.

332

234. Wild parsnip, *Pastinaca sativa* L.

Windsor, RL 19391

301 x 244 mm

NUMBERING: *335*

ANNOTATION: *Fiore e' seme de la Pastinaca, 788* ('Flower and seed of the parsnip. 788') [From Mattioli 1568, p. 788]

MOUNT SHEET: Type D

PROVENANCE: Sir Rex Nan Kivell

The wild parsnip is native to Europe and temperate regions of Asia, growing in fields at altitudes from sea level to 1,500m. The drawing shows only the upper portion of the plant, an erect stem bearing five flower clusters on long stalks, one of which has already gone to seed. The flowers are bright yellow in colour but not clearly delineated; one umbel is unfinished, consisting merely of a black chalk outline. The fruits are oval in shape with dark lines running along their axis.

The name *Pastinaca* derives from the Latin *pastus*, 'food' or 'sustenance', as the root of the parsnip was an important foodstuff in the Middle Ages. It was largely superseded by the carrot after that vegetable had been improved by breeding, but it has never disappeared from the table, especially in northern Europe. The fruit and root were distilled to prepare a specific for rheumatism, but contain toxic substances that can cause skin problems in sensitive subjects.

335
Fiore e' seme de la Pastinaca. 188

235. Valerian, *Valerianella* sp.

Windsor, RL 19455

247 x 196 mm

NUMBERING: *338*

MOUNT SHEET: Type D

PROVENANCE: Eliette Bostrom

This illustration shows some species of valerian, a plant of the family Valerianaceae. The genus *Valerianella* comprises many small annual plants with a short lifespan. The stem is erect, slender and noded, the leaves are narrow and linear, and small flowering branches grow from the upper nodes. Each inflorescence is made up of three or four groups of tiny flowers with brown calyxes and pink corollas divided into five petals.

236. Forking larkspur, *Consolida regalis* S.F. Gray

Windsor, RL 19456

251 x 180 mm. *Watermark*: Star 4

NUMBERING: *339*

MOUNT SHEET: Type D

PROVENANCE: Eliette Bostrom

The forking larkspur is a herbaceous annual of the family Ranunculaceae that can be found throughout Europe and temperate regions of western Asia. It infests grain fields and may have spread in ancient times together with the cultivation of wheat. A green dye can be obtained from the flowers and the plant was widely used for this purpose in Europe.

This drawing shows the upper part of the plant, a slender, branched stem with its fruit and flowers. The leaves which grow along the inflorescence are narrow and linear, while those along the main stem are palmate with deeply fringed margins. The flowers, made up of five petals and a long spur, are light blue with brownish shadows. The flowers, buds and fruits are borne on long, slender, erect stems. The fruit consists of an oblong follicle ending in a mucronate apex.

237. Eastern larkspur, *Consolida orientalis* (Gay) Schrödinger

Windsor, RL 19457

293 x 204 mm

NUMBERING: *340* (twice)

MOUNT SHEET: Type D

PROVENANCE: Eliette Bostrom

The eastern larkspur is a herbaceous annual of the family Ranunculaceae, originally from western and central Asia and eastern Europe and now cultivated as an ornamental and naturalized all over Europe. The eastern larkspur can often be found in a hybrid form with the rocket larkspur, *Consolida ajacis* (see **29**). The stem is slender and carries a large number of flowers with finely fringed bracts. The flower is made up of petaloid sepals and a pink corolla with a slightly curved spur. The lower part of the plant is not shown.

339

340
340

238. Mistletoe, *Viscum album* L.

Windsor, RL 19392

204 x 265 mm

NUMBERING: *354* (twice)

MOUNT SHEET: Type D

PROVENANCE: Sir Rex Nan Kivell

The mistletoe is a parasitic shrub belonging to the family Loranthaceae that grows widely in Europe, Asia and parts of North Africa, at altitudes from sea level to 1,200m. The stem shown here is dichotomous with short, straight branches, each bearing a pair of leaves at its distal end. The sessile, lanceolate leaves are dark green with three to five parallel veins that are a lighter green in colour. At the axil of each pair of leaves are one or two round, pearly-white berries. The detail at lower right shows two twigs, each carrying three sessile flowers whose corollas are made up of four rounded, light yellow petals.

The first record of *Viscum* is to be found in Pliny's *Historia naturalis*, which describes the rites and traditions associated with the mistletoe. Pliny noted that the Druids revered this strange plant which grew on the oak, a sacred tree in their religion. Because of this reference, Renaissance botanists tended to treat the mistletoe immediately after the oak in their herbals, but in fact mistletoe rarely grows on oak.

The word 'viscous' is derived from the Latin name for mistletoe, *viscum*, because a sticky liquid may be obtained from its bark that was once used as birdlime. The branches contain numerous compounds with medicinal properties, and preparations from the mistletoe were used to treat high blood pressure and nephritis, and as a sedative in epileptic patients and women suffering from nervous disturbances during the menopause. However, these treatments had to be administered with care since the plant contains toxic substances that may even be lethal in children.

354
354

239. Swallow wort, *Vincetoxicum hirundinaria* Medik. 1790

Windsor, RL 19393

289 x 249 mm

NUMBERING: *357*

MOUNT SHEET: Type D

PROVENANCE: Sir Rex Nan Kivell

The swallow wort is a herbaceous perennial of the family Asclepiadaceae, widespread in central, southern and eastern Europe, and in Algeria and Morocco. It grows on sunny cliffs and along the edges of forests from sea level to an altitude of 1,000m. This drawing shows the upper part of a plant in flower. It has an erect, smooth, tapering stem and opposite, lanceolate leaves with prominent veins. Each inflorescence is made up of a small number of white, five-petalled flowers growing on a long, slender peduncle from the axil of a pair of leaves.

The swallow wort was believed to be a cure for poisoning, and its generic name means 'vanquisher of toxins'. In truth it is itself poisonous. It was also believed that hanging a branch of swallow wort would protect one's house from being struck by lightning, and thus in the dialect of the Val d'Aosta it was known as *erba de troun* or 'thunder plant' (cf. **57**).

357

240. Hart's-tongue fern, *Asplenium scolopendrium* L.

Windsor, RL 19394

410 x 257 mm

NUMBERING: *369* [twice]

ANNOTATION: *Le frondi de la Phillitide, / gi*[*o*]*vano beuti al flusso del / corpo, a'carte. 879* ('The leaves of the *Phillitide* when drunk are beneficial for discharges of body fluids. 879') [From Mattioli 1568, pp. 879–80]

VERSO: sketch for the same (upside down)

MOUNT SHEET: Type D

PROVENANCE: Sir Rex Nan Kivell

The hart's-tongue fern is a perennial belonging to the family Aspleniaceae, common all over Europe, North Africa and Asia Minor and cultivated around the world. It is a water- and shade-loving species that grows in damp forests, among rocks and by bodies of water at altitudes from sea level to 1,000m. On the left is the upper side of a frond, a long blade with entire margins and a smooth, central rachis. Dark lines indicate the presence of clusters of spore-producing receptacles (sori) on the lower side. On the right is the underside of a frond with a rough, light green rachis with transverse rows of sori running along its length.

Dioscorides called the plant 'fillitide', writing that it was bitter to the taste and had neither stem nor flowers nor seeds. According to him the leaves steeped in wine offered an antidote to snake bite and were useful against dysentery. Mattioli added that water distilled with the leaves could be drunk to soothe the passions of the heart or to cure hiccups, and dried and powdered the leaves could alleviate liver and stomach pains.

369
369
Le frondi de la Phillitide
giovano beuti al flusso del
corpo, a'carte. 879

241. Yellow sorrel, *Oxalis corniculata* L.

Windsor, RL 19395

231 x 268 mm

NUMBERING: *371*

MOUNT SHEET: Type D

PROVENANCE: Sir Rex Nan Kivell

Yellow sorrel is a herbaceous perennial of the family Oxalidaceae, native to the Mediterranean and naturalized elsewhere. It grows in damp, uncultivated terrain and shady forests at altitudes from sea level to 800m. The scape is slender and carries three small flowers at its apex. The leaves, each consisting of three heart-shaped leaflets, grow from petioles that may be even longer than the scape. The one flower shown as fully open has six yellow petals (usually there are five); the stamens and pistils are not visible. There are four fruits consisting of long capsules with pointed mucrones. The plant has a short, thick, reddish taproot that ends in several rootlets.

The generic name used by Linnaeus, *Oxalis*, comes from the Greek οξύς (*oxys*), 'sharp/acidic', alluding to the taste of the leaves which, infused in water, were believed to have astringent, depurating and diuretic effects. The name had been used by Pliny, who in his *Historia naturalis* (Book 20, ch. 85) discusses 'Lapathum', the wild variety of which he says is called by some 'oxalis', but by 'our' people 'rumex'; but he described it as having pointed leaves, a colour like that of white beet and an extremely diminutive root, which suggests that he was not discussing the wood sorrel (*Oxalis acetosella*).

241

242. Fire lily, *Lilium bulbiferum* L.

London, Victoria and Albert Museum, E.735-1949

378 x 267 mm

NUMBERING: *384*

ANNOTATION: *Hÿacinthus Poeticus; Hemerocalle. cio e' / Giglio salvatico. La / radice trita. e' beuta. / e' messa con lana nè i, / pesoli provoca alle / donne l'acqua ragunata / nella madrice. e' il sangue / mestuo. mitigano le frondi / triti le infiamagioni delle / mamelle. dopo al parto. / e similmente quelle de / gli occhi, mettersi utilme= / nte le frondi. e la ra= / dice. su le cotture del / fuoco. 921.* ('Poet's hyacinth; *Hemerocalle*, that is wild lily. The root, minced and drunk and placed with wool in vaginal suppositories, induces the flow of the collected waters of the uterus [amniotic fluid] in women, and menstrual bleeding. The minced leaves mitigate the inflammation of the breasts after childbirth, and similarly that of the eyes. The leaves and root can usefully be placed over burns. 921.') [From Mattioli 1568, p. 921]

MOUNT SHEET: Type D

PROVENANCE: Helen de Beer

The fire lily is a bulbous herbaceous perennial belonging to the family Liliaceae, native to central and southern Europe, where it grows in sub-Alpine meadows, tall vegetation and copses at altitudes between 500m and 1,900m. Lilies have been cultivated for millennia as an ornamental plant: they can be recognized on Minoan vases and frescos, and were grown in gardens all over Europe from the sixteenth century. The generic name *Lilium* comes from the Greek λείριον (*leirion*), used by Theophrastus and Hippocrates for the white lily, *Lilium candidum*.

The stem is erect and smooth with sessile leaves growing along its length. The leaves are linear in form with entire margins and acute apices. At the apex of the stem are four flowers on long, thick peduncles, one still closed, one in full bloom and two from which the petals have dropped away, exposing their reproductive parts. The flowers have orange tepals that are streaked with a lighter colour on their inner surfaces, six stamens with long, dark orange filaments and an orange stylus emanating from a long, narrow ovary and ending in a small, flattened stigma. To the right is the bulb, which has white tunics and roots growing from both base and apex.

Hyacintus Poeticus
Hemerocalle. cio è
Giglio saluatico. La
radice trita. e beuta.
e messa con lana ne i
pessoli prouoca alle
donne l'acqua ragunata
nella matrice. e il sangue
mestruo. mitigano le frondi
triti le infiamagioni delle
mamelle. dopo al parto.
e similmente quelle de
gli occhi, mettensi utilme=
nte le frondi. e le ra=
dice. su le cotture del
fuoco. 921.
384

242a. Scarlet martagon lily, *Lilium chalcedonicum* L.

Private collection, UK

Pen and ink over black chalk

375 x 270 mm

NUMBERING: *387*

ANNOTATION: *Hemorocalle Gostantinopolitano / overo Riccio de la gran Sig[nor]*[a] */ nacque lanno 1620 nel copiosissimo giardino del Mag[nifi]*[co] *Sig[no]*[r] *Pelegrino Pele= / grini perugino Ecc[ellentissimo] professore de semplici / con un fusto largo dacapo doi onci / e'da piedi largo un oncia, vicino alla / radice era di colore lionato oscuro / è dacapo apena si conioscevano 25 / fusti oniti insieme, li fiori erano / 25 è di colore belisimo, era tutta / la pianta alta 4 piedi, fiore veramente / bellisimo, mai piu visto ne scritto da nisuno. / Molti professori di tal scientia andetto che / è mostro overo acidente de la Natura* ('Lily of Constantinople, or Curl of the Great Lady. It grew in the year 1620 in the abundant garden of the illustrious Signor Pellegrino Pellegrini of Perugia, most excellent professor of simples, with a stem two inches wide at the top and one inch wide at the foot. Close to the root it was dark tawny in colour, and at the top were 25 stems joined together that could barely be distinguished. There were 25 flowers of a most beautiful colour. The whole plant was 4 feet high, a truly beautiful flower never seen since or written about by anyone. Many professors of this subject have said that it is a monster or accident of nature')

MOUNT SHEET: Type D

PROVENANCE: Gerta Calmann; Christie's (New York), 28 January 2000, lot 18

This is a teratological form of a lily affected by fasciation, its round stem broadened and flattened in the manner of many stems fused together. It is a condition that may affect a range of plants, including the broccoli depicted in **291** and the artichoke in **293** (similarly labelled 'monstrous'). It is commonly found in lilies and is well documented in *Lilium martagon*: Tabernaemontanus illustrated the phenomenon on p. 640 of the *Eicones Plantarum* of 1590 (comp. fig. 242a; see Fig. 10, p. 29, for the normal form in Dodoens's herbal of 1583). *Hemerocalle Costantinopolitano*, however, was the species now known as *Lilium chalcedonicum*, the scarlet martagon lily, of Near Eastern and Balkan origin. The flower has been widely cultivated in European gardens since the sixteenth century, and in Italy is now naturalized in the Chianti and Mugello regions of Tuscany.

Comp. fig. 242a. Martagon lily (*Lilium martagon*). J. Theodorus (Tabernaemontanus), *Eicones plantarum*, Frankfurt 1590, p. 640

Unlike most of the sheets in the *Erbario Miniato* corpus (**1–277**), the drawing carries Cesi's own comments on the plant rather than passages copied from Mattioli's 1568 *Discorsi*. It is also notable for being the only drawing in the *Erbario* corpus executed in pen and ink (but cf. **293**) and to bear a date (1620). This was the year in which the lily was grown, rather than the date of execution of the drawing, but it may be assumed that the drawing was made not long after. While the sheet therefore does not seem to have been part of the same campaign of illustration as the bulk

Hemorocalle Gostantinopolitano
ouero Riccio de la Gran Sig.ʳᵃ
nacque l'anno 1620, nel copiosissimo
giardino del Mag.ᶜᵒ Sig.ʳ Pelegrino Pele=
grini perugino Ecc: professore de semplici.
con un fusto largo da capo. doi onci
è darsi di largo un onica, vicino alla
radice era di colore lionato oscuro
è da capo apena si conoscevano 25
fusti oniti insieme, li fiori erano
25. è di colore belissimo, era tutta
la pianta alta 4 piedi, fiore veramente
belissimo, mai piu visto ne scritto da nisuno.
Molti professori di tal scientia an detto cke
è mostro ouero acidente de la Natura
347

242a

of the *Erbario*, the 'Pozzo' number *387* indicates that it was placed with the other lilies in the *Erbario* sequence (**242–244**, which bear 'Pozzo' numbers *384–388*). The section on lilies in Mattioli's *Discorsi*, *'Dell'Hemerocalle, cio è, Giglio salvatico'*, begins on p. 921, as cited by Cesi on **242**. It is uncertain whether the sheet was inserted into the *Erbario* sequence by Cesi himself, or later by Cassiano or Carlo Antonio (who were responsible for the 'Pozzo' numbering).

Cesi's note refers to Pellegrino Pellegrini, professor of simples at the University of Perugia (not far from Cesi's residence at Acquasparta; cf. **113**) from at least 1609. Pellegrini was responsible for teaching the practice of simples, while his colleague Annibale Camilli was in charge of teaching theory (see Mariotti MS). The university had no botanical garden of its own at this time, so gardens belonging to the professors were used for classes.

243. Lily of the valley, *Convallaria majalis* L.

Present location unknown

362 x 263 mm

NUMBERING: *388*

MOUNT SHEET: Type D

PROVENANCE: Boone sale, lot 133

The lily of the valley is a herbaceous perennial that bears its overwintering buds underground. A member of the family Liliaceae, it is widespread throughout Europe and temperate zones of Asia, growing in broadleaved forests at altitudes to about 1,200m, and is cultivated and naturalized throughout the world (see also **244**). This drawing shows a specimen in full flower. Broad lanceolate leaves envelop the stem, which is robust with paired bracts growing from its nodes. The slight floral scape carries flowers on slender peduncles with linear bracts. The perianths have slightly reflexed lobes and are white in colour with an unusual faint pink tinge.

The common names for this plant in Italian (*mughetto*) and French (*muguet*) derive from the Latin *muscatus*, 'scented with musk'. Formerly known as *Lilium convallium*, the scientific name which it was eventually assigned refers both to the valleys where this species may be found and to the fact that it flowers in the month of May. The plant was also known as *giglio di maggio* ('May lily') and as *lacrime della Madonna* ('Our Lady's tears'), its flowers symbolizing the tears shed by the Virgin beneath the Cross. The plant was used to prepare nostrums against the most disparate of ills, from colds to dropsy to impotence. Its effects are similar to that of the foxglove (**201**), and it is likewise poisonous but may be administered over longer periods of time.

388

244. Lily of the valley, *Convallaria majalis* L.

Present location unknown

377 x 257 mm; drawing on right cut from another sheet and pasted on to the folio

NUMBERING: *388*

MOUNT SHEET: Type D

PROVENANCE: Boone sale, lot 133

This drawing depicts two further specimens of the lily of the valley (see **243**). In the drawing on the right (silhouetted and pasted to the page) the root system is shown, a white rhizome with numerous fine rootlets. The artist also shows the tiny bract that subtends each flower which, as in **243**, is white stained with pink.

244

245. Lady orchid, *Orchis purpurea* Huds.

Present location unknown

NUMBERING: *391* (twice)

ANNOTATION: *Un altro testicolo; Orchis Pratense; Sono di piu sorte li testicoli di / cane. questa impiastrata risolve / le posteme mondifica l'ulcere / e' no*[*n*] *le lascia corodere: sana le fistole / e' mitiga le infiamagione, beute con vino / ristagneno il corpo, 929; N:º 52* ('Another *testicolo*; field orchid; there are many sorts of "dog's testicles". This one applied as a poultice resolves abscesses, clears ulcers and stops them festering. It cures fistulas and mitigates inflammation. Drunk with wine, it stabilizes the body. 929. No. 52') [From Mattioli 1568, p. 929]

The lady orchid is a species of the family Orchidaceae, found throughout Europe and Asia in thickets and clearings and in the undergrowth of forests and olive groves, from sea level to an altitude of 1,800m. The name *Orchis* comes from the Greek ὀρχις (*orchis*), 'testicle', a reference to the form of the plant's pseudobulbs; following the doctrine of signatures, orchids were thus considered to be aphrodisiacs. The lady orchid is one of several species whose bulbs are dried and ground to a powder to make *salep*, a spice that is added to many Middle Eastern dishes and drinks.

The entire plant is shown, with its inflorescence and roots. This specimen has a robust, slightly curved scape and four broad, linear leaves with entire margins and acute apices that envelop the scape at its base. The lower and underground parts of the stem are white; the root system consists of two slender, ovoid tubers surmounted by fine rootlets. The flowers are arranged in a dense, cone-shaped spike. Each flower has a broad labellum with a large central lobe flanked by two smaller lobes that are white, faintly variegated with purple. The tepals are darker in colour and converge to form a galea. At lower left the artist has drawn two slightly enlarged flowers, in which the form of the labellum and the segmented perianth can be more clearly seen. At upper right is another flower drawn in profile, without its tepals, showing the curved white spur of the flower. Next to this is a detail of a small, ovate-lanceolate bract.

The annotation copies some of Dioscorides' observations on p. 929 of the *Discorsi* ('Di un'altro Testicolo'), but the illustration on the same page ('Spetie di Testicolo II') shows an indeterminate species of the genus *Ophrys* (see **246**). *Orchis purpurea* is illustrated on p. 932 ('Spetie di Testicolo V'), where Mattioli also explains the origin of the name, from 'the two bulbs similar to two testicles' ('due radici simili a due testicoli').

391
unaltro testicol
Orchis Pratense
Sono di piu sorte li testicoli di
cane. questa impiastrata risolue
le posteme, mondifica l'ulcere
e no le lascia corrodere: sana le fistole
e mitiga le infiamagione: beute con vino
ristagneno il corpo, 929
N.o 52
391

246. Bee orchid, *Ophrys apifera* Huds.

Private collection

291 x 249 mm. *Watermark*: Fleur de lys on hills, in circle, with surmounting letter M (type of Fleur de lys 44–55)

NUMBERING: *392* (twice)

ANNOTATION: *Testicolo Apino* (twice); *orchis Apiformìs flore Purpurascen*[–]; *Purpurascente; Spetie de Testicoli / la cui virtu è inunaltro; 929* ('Bee *testicolo*; reddish-flowered bee-shaped orchid; reddish; type of *testicolo* whose quality is found in another. 929') [From Mattioli 1568, p. 929]

PROVENANCE: Boone sale, lot 138

LITERATURE: *Quaderni Puteani* 1, pp. 57 (fig. 38), 60

The bee orchid is a bulbous herbaceous perennial belonging to the family Orchidaceae, commonly found throughout south, west and central Europe, in grassland and clearings at altitudes from sea level to 800m.

The entire plant is shown. The pseudobulb, which is quite small in comparison to the plant itself, is oval in form with a yellowish tunic and a small bulbil, and with roots growing from its upper part. The stem of the plant is thick, erect and white, with dark green leaves growing alternately along its length. The leaves are narrowly elliptical with entire margins, acute apices and parallel veins running along their length. The spike comprises three flowers growing from the axils of long bracts, with pink tepals and broad labellums that are brownish in colour with an irregular yellow pattern. The reproductive structures cannot be seen.

The generic name *Ophrys* comes from the Greek οφρύς (*ophrys*), 'eyebrow'. According to Pliny some orchids contained a pigment that was used by Greek women to darken their eyebrows, though the reason for the name may also be the shape of the segments to be found within the perigonium. The specific epithet *apifera* is based on the resemblance of the labellum to the bee.

An orchid species which cannot be identified with precision is illustrated by Mattioli on p. 929 of his *Discorsi*, the page cited by Cesi. The reference to 'another' plant with which the present 'testicle' shares its medicinal properties may be to the 'other testicle' drawn on **245** ('Un'altro testicolo'), where Cesi copied out a passage on medicinal usage from Dioscorides' chapter 'Di un'altro Testicolo' (*I Discorsi*, p. 929).

392
Testicolo Apino
Testicolo Apino..
Orchis Apiformis flore Purpurascen
Purpura scente
Spetie de Testicoli
929
392

247. French honeysuckle, *Hedysarum coronarium* L.

Windsor, RL 19396
227 x 265 mm
NUMBERING: *401*
MOUNT SHEET: Type D
PROVENANCE: Sir Rex Nan Kivell

French honeysuckle is a herbaceous perennial of the family Fabaceae. Originally from North Africa and Spain, growing in clay and subsaline soils at altitudes from sea level to 1,200m, it is now cultivated as an ornamental and for fodder; it is naturalized throughout the Mediterranean. The first references to the species in central Europe date from the beginning of the seventeenth century, when it was exported from Spain as an ornamental plant; its Italian common name *sulla* seems to be derived from the Castilian word for the plant, *zulla*.

The stem of this twining plant is thick, curved and tapering. The leaves are alternate and composed of seven ovate leaflets with entire margins. From the axil of each leaf grows a smaller branch bearing a terminal raceme of red papilionaceous flowers. At lower left is a detail of a single flower, in which the toothed calyx can be seen.

247

248. Yellow water lily, *Nuphar lutea* (L.) Sibth. & Sm.

Windsor, RL 19397

NUMBERING: *404*

Two sheets joined horizontally: upper sheet 179 x 251 mm; lower sheet 98 x 251 mm

Watermark: Lamb in circle

MOUNT SHEET: Type D

PROVENANCE: Sir Rex Nan Kivell

LITERATURE: Freedberg 1989, pp. 47, 51 (fig. 12); *Quaderni Puteani* 4, p. 194 (cat. 118); *Cassiano* cat. 1997, p. 32 (cat. 61); Freedberg 2002, pp. 22, 26 (fig. 1.14)

The yellow water lily is a perennial water plant belonging to the family Nymphaeaceae. It is common throughout Europe and Asia Minor, growing in still or slow-flowing waters at altitudes from sea level to 1,500m, and is cultivated in all the temperate regions of the world. The generic name *Nuphar* derives from the Persian *ninûfar*, a plant which was known to the ancient Greeks and was described by Dioscorides. In Italian (*ninfea*) and French (*nymphéa*) this plant is named after the nymphs of Greek mythology, among whom were the naiads, associated with springs and streams. The yellow water lily exudes a scent reminiscent of stale alcohol and its seed capsule resembles a miniature liquor flask, which is why the plant is popularly known in some languages as the 'brandy bottle'.

Five flowers are shown to demonstrate their development, on two pieces of paper pasted together. At lower centre is a closed bud. At upper left is a flower in full bloom growing on a thick, erect stem. Its five broad, rounded petals are bright yellow with undulating margins; they surround a dense cluster of stamens with yellow anthers and filaments and a yellow, disc-shaped stigma, and at the lower left is a full-blown flower that is just beginning to wilt. At upper right is a flower that has reached a more mature stage: the petals open more widely, the swollen ovary is still green but has assumed its characteristic flask shape, and the twelve radial septa of the stigma are clearly visible. At the base of the ovary is a ring consisting of the stamens' filaments, now dried and curved. Finally, at lower right, is a mature seed capsule, brown in colour and surrounded by its dried petals.

248

249. [?] Crown daisy, *Glebionis coronaria* (L.) Cassini ex Spach

Present location unknown

143 x 235 mm

NUMBERING: *414*

MOUNT SHEET: Type D

This is possibly the crown daisy, *Glebionis coronaria* (see **185**), although not enough of the plant's characteristics are shown to allow a definite identification. The stem is erect and slender and terminates in a bright yellow flower head. Along the lower two-thirds of its length are numerous alternate leaves with short, slightly erect petioles. The leaves are elliptical in form and deeply indented into seven lobes with finely toothed margins. The flower head has a peripheral corona of ligulate flowers.

249

250. Ox-eye daisy, *Leucanthemum vulgare* Lam. 1778

Windsor, RL 19398

363 x 265 mm

NUMBERING: *415*

ANNOTATION: *Bellis Magiore. 960* ('Greater *Bellis*. 960') [From Mattioli 1568, p. 960]

MOUNT SHEET: Type D

PROVENANCE: Sir Rex Nan Kivell

The ox-eye daisy (or moon daisy) is a herbaceous perennial of the family Asteraceae, common throughout Europe (except Spain). It flourishes close to human habitations, in fields and along roadsides, and more rarely in wild pastures and forest clearings, at altitudes from sea level to 2,000m. The stem is erect, smooth and branching in its upper part. The leaves are alternate, sessile and narrowly lanceolate with toothed margins. Each branch ends in a capitulum of white ligulate flowers surrounding a cluster of tiny yellow tubulose flowers.

Bunches of the ox-eye daisy were hung above the doorways of haylofts to ward off lightning. The plant has no medicinal properties, although it was once employed in the adulteration of a drug distilled from *Pyrethrum* (= *Tanacetum*) *cinerariifolium*.

The ox-eye daisy was assigned to the genus *Leucanthemum* by Tournefort, in the early eighteenth century, and his successor Linnaeus transferred it to the burgeoning genus *Chrysanthemum*. In the late twentieth century an attempt was made to break up the genus (see **185**), and many former chrysanthemums, such as this one, are now to be found in other genera. The illustration on p. 960 of Mattioli's *Discorsi*, cited in the annotation, shows one of the *Leucanthemum vulgare* complex of species, perhaps *Leucanthemum praecox*.

Bellis Magiore . 960
415

251. Daisy, *Bellis perennis* L.

Windsor, RL 19399

Two sheets joined horizontally: upper sheet 163 x 232 mm; lower sheet 110 x 232 mm

NUMBERING: *416* (twice)

MOUNT SHEET: Type D

PROVENANCE: Sir Rex Nan Kivell

The daisy is a herbaceous perennial of the family Asteraceae, common all over Europe and temperate parts of Asia to an altitude of 1,200m. The artist has drawn two plants complete with their roots. The stem of the upper specimen is short and its spatulate leaves grow in a rosette at its base. The scapes are long, slender, pinkish in colour and slightly hairy. The involucre is not clearly drawn but consists of linear bracts. The flower head is made up of an internal cluster of yellow flowers surrounded by a circle of ligulate flowers, white with undersides streaked with pink. The roots are slender and branching.

The specimen below, drawn on a separate piece of paper, has leaves that are broadly toothed rather than entire, and smooth scapes. The flower heads have scale-like bracts and are made up of pink tubulose flowers. The roots appear to be densely branching and clustered.

The generic name of the daisy, *Bellis*, is probably derived from the Latin *bellus*, 'beautiful'. Pliny the Elder mentioned the flower, but it was passed over by Theophrastus, Dioscorides and Galen. Later herbalists used it to heal wounds and as a remedy for lung and throat illnesses.

416

252. Spotted globe daisy, *Globularia punctata* Lapeyr.; hen-and-chickens, *Bellis perennis* L. cv. 'Prolifera'; daisy, *Bellis perennis* L. cv.

Windsor, RL 19400

308 x 264 mm; upper two drawings cut from another sheet and pasted on to the folio

NUMBERING: *417*

ANNOTATION: *Bellis Cerulea Montana; Bellis Prolifera; Bellis Flore uariegato Pleno* ('Blue mountain *Bellis;* prolific *Bellis;* full-flowering variegated *Bellis*')

MOUNT SHEET: Type D

PROVENANCE: Sir Rex Nan Kivell

LITERATURE: *Quaderni Puteani* 4, p. 199 (cat. 122)

This drawing shows, at upper left and upper centre, two specimens of the spotted globe daisy, together with some cultivated varieties of the common daisy.

The spotted globe daisy is a herbaceous perennial of the family Globulariaceae, widespread in central and southern Europe in dry pastures at altitudes from sea level to 1,500m. A capitulum of blue flowers grows from the apex of an erect, slightly sinuous scape. The alternate, sessile leaves are lanceolate with entire margins and pointed tips. The generic name *Globularia* refers to the rounded form of the flower head. Its leaves are used as a diuretic and purgative.

Below are four cultivars of the daisy (see **251**) with variegated red flower heads. At lower left is the hen-and-chickens, called by Gerard the 'childing daisy', *Bellis perennis* cv. 'Prolifera'. Its unusual inflorescence consists of a central bundle of green flowers surrounded by numerous circles of ligulate pink flowers. From its base grow six smaller flower heads on erect stems, surrounding the main capitulum. The other three specimens have single flower heads with a bundle of yellowish-green flowers at their centres. The overlapping linear bracts of the capitulum are visible in the drawing on the right. Here, as on several other sheets from the dismantled companion volume to the *Erbario Miniato*, the annotations seem to be in an eighteenth-century hand emulating Cesi's handwriting, and may well record an early inscription that was trimmed off when the sheet was cut down.

Bellis Cerulea Montana
Bellis Prolifera
Bellis Flore uariegato Pleno

253. Peony, *Paeonia mascula* (L.) Mill. with the root of *Paeonia officinalis* L.

Windsor, RL 19401

362 x 270 mm; roots of the flower cut from another sheet and inlaid

NUMBERING: *419*

MOUNT SHEET: Type D

PROVENANCE: Sir Rex Nan Kivell

LITERATURE: *Quaderni Puteani* 1, pp. 61, 63, 69 (fig. 48); *Quaderni Puteani* 4, p. 192 (cat. 117); *Cassiano* cat. 1997, p. 32 (cat. 60); *Fiori* cat. 2004, pp. 182–4 (fig. 3); *Amazing Rare Things* 2007, p. 102 (pl. 35)

The peony is a flowering plant of the family Ranunculaceae that may be found throughout southern Europe (see also **254–255**). This illustration is a composite of two species of peony, a flowering branch of *Paeonia mascula* on which has been pasted the root of *P. officinalis*. The stem is thick, smooth and brownish. The leaf grows from a long petiole and is composed of a blade divided into lanceolate lobes with pointed tips, entire margins and brown veins. The flower is made up of rounded petals, pale red with a fine network of darker veins. The blossom has a large number of stamens carrying brownish-yellow anthers; at its centre can be glimpsed silky, pubescent pistils with red stigmas. Five elongated tubers grow from the distinctive root of *Paeonia officinalis*.

The peony may have been named after Paion, the physician of the gods to whom Pliny the Elder attributed the discovery of the curative properties of this plant. The Greeks used it to treat asthma, gout, madness and epilepsy in children. Theophrastus warned herbalists to gather the plant at night to avoid being seen and attacked by the woodpecker, to whom the plant was sacred. The use of the plant for medicinal purposes was gradually abandoned because it also contains toxic substances.

254. Peony, *Paeonia officinalis* L. cv.

Collection of Patti Skouras, USA

405 x 256 mm

NUMBERING: *420*

MOUNT SHEET: Type D

PROVENANCE: Boone sale, lot 132

Here and in the following drawing the artist has depicted a cultivar of the peony (see **253**). The leaves are deeply indented into long, narrow lobes with entire margins. The flower is made up of bright red, irregularly rounded petals with a calyx of lanceolate sepals.

255. Peony, *Paeonia officinalis* L. cv.

Collection of Patti Skouras, USA

364 x 267 mm. *Watermark*: Fleur de lys on hills, in circle, with surmounting letter M (type of Fleur de lys 44–55)

NUMBERING: *421*

MOUNT SHEET: Type D

PROVENANCE: Boone sale, lot 132

See **254**.

419

421

256. Laburnum, *Laburnum anagyroides* Medik. 1787

Private collection

276 x 270 mm

NUMBERING: *426* (twice)

MOUNT SHEET: Type D

PROVENANCE: Boone sale, lot 134

The laburnum is a small tree belonging to the family Fabaceae that is native to central and southern Europe, where it grows in forests of oak and chestnut at altitudes from sea level to 1,000m. It has been cultivated since the end of the sixteenth century, both for decoration and for its hard, flexible wood. The plant is extremely poisonous (about two dozen pods being sufficient to cause death in an adult) since all of its parts contain an alkaloid, cytisine, that is absorbed rapidly and causes paralysis of the nervous system.

The stem of this specimen carries five leaves and a pendulous inflorescence. The leaves are composed of three lanceolate segments that are equal in size. The flowers have short calyxes and yellow papilionaceous corollas; the reproductive structures are not shown. The seed pods, shown in a detail at lower right, are slightly knobbed and irregular in shape.

426
426

257. [?] Brookweed, *Samolus valerandi* L.

Private collection

261 x 236 mm

NUMBERING: *427*

MOUNT SHEET: Type D

PROVENANCE: Sir Rex Nan Kivell

The stem of this plant is erect, smooth and branching at its base. Each branch bears numerous alternate leaves that are ovate-spatulate in form with short stems, entire margins and rounded apices. At the apex of the stem are five flowers, each carried on a long peduncle that springs from the axil of a leaf. The corollas are composed of five white petals, but the calyx and reproductive structures are not visible. The underground portion consists of a taproot with many long, fine rootlets. This may be the brookweed, a member of the family Primulaceae, although that species has a rosette of basal leaves, a more luxuriant inflorescence and longer pedicels than seen here.

427

258. Perforate St John's wort, *Hypericum perforatum* L.

Present location unknown
257 x 266 mm
NUMBERING: *428*
MOUNT SHEET: Type D
PROVENANCE: Boone sale, lot 136

St John's wort is a herbaceous perennial of the family Clusiaceae, native to Europe, Asia and North Africa, and now naturalized throughout the world. It grows in arid pastures, in undergrowth and along the edges of forests and roads, to an altitude of 1,600m. The drawing shows the upper part of the plant. The erect stem branches at its apex; along the stem are narrow, elliptical leaves in opposite pairs on short petioles. Each branch ends in a yellow flower of five elliptical petals covered with black glandular structures. A large number of yellow stamens can be seen at the centres of the corollas; their pistils are not visible. When the flowers are picked a dark red latex seeps from the broken stems, and the leaves appear to be perforated by tiny holes – actually glands containing essential oils.

Since ancient times magical properties have been attributed to the plant. It was supposed to protect those who carried it against lightning and harm by the devil, and Mattioli cited the name *caccia diavoli*, or 'devil chaser' (*I Discorsi*, p. 990). The generic name *Hypericum* comes from Dioscorides and Hippocrates, who called it υπέρεικον (*ypereikon*) to intimate that it was 'above' or stronger than any malign force. The name St John's wort refers to St John the Baptist (the latex being the blood of his martyrdom), whose feast day is 24 June, as the plant was anciently associated with the celebration of the summer solstice. Another English name was 'balm of the warrior', as the oils of the plant have cicatrizing properties and can be used to treat wounds and burns. The plant has also been used to treat shingles, bronchial and urinary tract infections, and bedsores; more recently its effectiveness as a remedy for nervous disorders, particularly depression, has also been claimed.

258

259. Tutsan, *Hypericum androsaemum* L.

Private collection

252 x 228 mm

NUMBERING: *429*

ANNOTATION: *Androsemum Maius / sive Hÿpericon Maximū* ('Greater *Androsemum* or great *Hypericum*')

MOUNT SHEET: Type D (trimmed)

PROVENANCE: Sir Rex Nan Kivell

Tutsan is a perennial shrub of the family Clusiaceae that grows widely in central and southern Europe, Asia Minor and Tunisia; it has also been naturalized in Australia, New Zealand and Chile. It thrives in forests and damp, shady areas from sea level to altitudes of 1,400m.

This drawing shows two plants, one in flower and the other with its fruit. The stem is erect and smooth, with broad, ovate, sessile leaves with entire margins and tapering apices. The stem on the right terminates in an umbel of five flowers, each composed of five rounded yellow petals. The specimen on the left has a reddish stem and bright red, oval berries growing from the ends of long peduncles; each is subtended by three or more oval bracts.

Tutsan contains the same active principles as the related St John's wort (see **258**), and it too was considered to have healing powers and was used to treat wounds and to kill parasitic worms – its English name comes from the Italian *tuttasana*, 'all health'. An illustration of the plant appears on p. 986 of the *Discorsi*, and Mattioli recorded both the names 'Androsemum' ('male seed') and 'Hiperico' (see **258**) given here.

The inscriptions for this and the following drawing (**260**) appear to be in an eighteenth-century hand, recording Cesi's original annotations.

Androsemum Maius
siue Hypericon Maximū
429

260. Purple loosestrife, *Lythrum salicaria* L.

Windsor, RL 19402

354 x 195 mm. *Watermark*: indistinct

NUMBERING: *435*

ANNOTATION: *Lisimachia Purpurea* ('Purple *Lisimachia*')

MOUNT SHEET: Type D (cut down)

PROVENANCE: Sir Rex Nan Kivell

Purple loosestrife is a herbaceous perennial of the family Lythraceae that grows in wet habitats from sea level to an altitude of 1,200m. The erect, slender, reddish-brown stem bears opposite leaves that are narrowly lanceolate with entire margins and acute apices. It terminates in a raceme of dark pink flowers composed of five elongated petals; their stamens and pistils cannot be seen.

The generic name *Lythrum* comes from the Greek λύθρον (*lythron*), meaning 'black blood' or 'impure blood in a woman's womb', and may refer to the purple colour of the flowers or to the plant's medicinal properties. Dioscorides recommended loosestrife in cases of excessive menstrual flow, and to aid the healing of wounds. The plant was illustrated by Mattioli (p. 999) under the name 'Lisimachia' (see **267**), as here.

Lisimachia Purpurea
435

261. Angular Solomon's seal, *Polygonatum odoratum* (Mill.) Druce

Windsor, RL 19403

313 x 266 mm. *Watermark*: Fleur de lys 55

NUMBERING: *438* (twice)

MOUNT SHEET: Type D

PROVENANCE: Sir Rex Nan Kivell

The angular Solomon's seal is a herbaceous perennial, similar to the lily of the valley (**243–244**), of the family Liliaceae. It is common throughout Europe and Asia, growing in thickets and coppices and along the edges of dry forests at altitudes from 1,200m to 1,500m. The stem is erect and robust and grows from a thick horizontal rhizome. The leaves are alternate and elliptical in form with entire margins and pointed apices. Growing on long pedicels from the axils of the upper leaves are three flower buds. On the left is a detail of a twig with three round black berries hanging from long branching pedicels.

The generic name comes from the Greek πολύς (*polys*), 'many', and γονύ (*gony*) or γονάτιον (*gonation*), 'knee', 'joint' or 'knot', a reference to the knobbly appearance of the root. According to legend King Solomon left the mark of his seal upon the plant, in the cross-section of the root. In accordance with the doctrine of signatures, a preparation of the root dissolved in water was applied to fractured bones. Dioscorides noted that applying the dried root to wounds could speed their healing. The berries of the plant are poisonous and may be used as a drastic emetic.

430
438

262. Bulbous comfrey, *Symphytum bulbosum* K.F. Schimp.; common comfrey, *Symphytum officinale* L.

Windsor, RL 32571

310 x 271 mm

NUMBERING: *443*

ANNOTATION: *Consolida magiore; Consolida Media~~aggiore~~ e' molto utile p*[*er*] *le Rotture intestinali / e' esteriori, e' similmente p*[*er*] *consolidare lulcere e' le ferite*. ('Greater *Consolida*; ~~Greater~~ medium *Consolida* is useful for intestinal and external ruptures, and likewise for healing ulcers and wounds.') [From Mattioli 1568, pp. 1012–13]

MOUNT SHEET: Type D

PROVENANCE: Dudley Snelgrove; from whose heirs purchased, 1993

This sheet shows two species of comfrey, herbaceous perennials of the family Boraginaceae. The main drawing is the bulbous comfrey, native to Europe and some temperate regions of Asia, where it can be found growing in damp terrain. The stem is erect and covered with tiny hairs. The alternate leaves are broadly lanceolate with conspicuous veins. The flowers, some in full bloom and others just beginning to wilt, are arranged in lax bilateral clusters carried on long petioles. The calyx is slightly toothed and the tubulose corolla is yellow. The scales of the corolla, a useful diagnostic character, seem to extend a considerable distance from the throat of the flower.

The detail at lower right shows an inflorescence of the common comfrey, with pink, scaleless blooms. This plant is widespread in eastern and southern Europe, where it grows in forests, beneath hedges and in uncultivated fields from sea level to an altitude of 1,000m.

The generic name *Symphytum* comes from the Greek συμφύω (*symphyo*), 'to fuse or unite' (hence also its Italian name *consolida*), referring to the supposed healing properties of these plants. The root of the common comfrey was employed as a sweetener and in remedies for diarrhoea and throat infections, though the plant is poisonous. In the past the plant was treated with bismuth to obtain a brown dye.

The annotation copies a passage from p. 1013 of *I Discorsi*, where the 'Consolida media' is illustrated (see Fig. 14, p. 34). That print corresponds neither to bulbous nor to common comfrey, but probably to the pyramid bugle, *Ajuga pyramidalis*. The common comfrey was correctly identified in the inscription with Mattioli's 'Consolida maggiore' illustrated on the preceding page.

Consolida maggiore
443
Consolida Media Maggiore. e molto utile p le Rotture intestinali
e esteriori, e similmente p conso lidare lulcere e le ferite.

262

263. Cinquefoil, *Geum urbanum* L.

Present location unknown

308 x 265 mm

NUMBERING: *456*

ANNOTATION: *Gariophillata si crede p[er] testimonio / dell' aromatico odore che ha la radice, / che sia pianta de non poco valore* ('*Gariophillata*; it is believed, from the evidence of the aromatic scent of the root, that this is a plant of no little value') [From Mattioli 1568, pp. 1036–7]

MOUNT SHEET: Type D

PROVENANCE: Boone sale, lot 136

These three drawings depict the cinquefoil with its flowers and fruit, its root system and a detail of its flower. A member of the family Rosaceae, the plant may be found throughout Europe, growing in abandoned fields and broadleaved forests at altitudes from sea level to 1,600m.

The stem is slender, branching and reflexed at its distal end. The leaves are alternate and deeply divided into three to five lobes with toothed margins and acute apices. Each branch terminates in either a flower composed of five rounded yellow petals or a cluster of achenes. The root is broad at its base but rapidly tapers, ending in numerous fine rootlets. The rhizomatous root can be used as a bitter tonic and astringent in cases of gastrointestinal atony.

456
Gariophillata si crede p testimonio
dell'aromatico odore che ha la radice,
che sia pianta de non poco valore

264. Italian viper's bugloss, *Echium italicum* L.

Windsor, RL 19404

244 x 266 mm

NUMBERING: *467*

MOUNT SHEET: Type D

ANNOTATION: [cut]

PROVENANCE: Sir Rex Nan Kivell

Italian viper's bugloss is a herbaceous biennial of the family Boraginaceae, common in southern and western Europe, in temperate regions of Asia, and in Egypt and Libya and naturalized elsewhere, growing in arid areas from sea level to an altitude of 1,300m. The erect, robust stem bears subopposite, sessile leaves that are linear in form with entire margins and acute apices. Both the stem and leaves are covered with long, erect hairs. Near the apex, immature pale blue flowers, terminating in five rounded shallow lobes, grow from the axils of the leaves.

The generic name is derived from the Greek ἔχις (*echis*), 'viper'. Using the doctrine of signatures, Mattioli claimed that *Echium italicum* was the most effective remedy against snake bite because the seed was similar to the form of the viper's head (p. 1050). In fact, the Italian viper's bugloss has no medicinal properties. The plant was illustrated on p. 1048 of the *Discorsi*.

264

265. Meadow grass, *Poa pratensis* L.; couch grass, *Cynodon dactylon* (L.) Pers. 1805

Private collection

324 x 256 mm. *Watermark*: Fleur de lys 51

NUMBERING: *470* [twice]

ANNOTATION: *fiori de gramegna* ('grass flowers')

MOUNT SHEET: Type D

PROVENANCE: Sir Rex Nan Kivell

The artist may have believed that he was portraying two parts of the same plant on this sheet, but he has in fact drawn the inflorescence of the meadow grass, and at lower right a stolon of couch grass. Both are herbaceous perennials of the family Poaceae. They reproduce vegetatively by sending down subterranean stolons which, when they emerge, form characteristic tufts of grass, and though they can be invasive and infesting weeds, both are grown for forage and fodder.

Meadow grass is a Eurasian species that is now naturalized in all the temperate zones of the globe. The stem grass is slender and erect with short, narrow leaves and terminates in an ample panicle of spikelets. The generic name *Poa* comes from the Greek πόα, a term used for grass fodder in Homer, Hesiod and Herodotus.

Couch grass, originally from Europe, is now also cosmopolitan. The specimen consists of a vertical stem with short, linear leaves and a horizontal white stolon that has roots growing from its nodes. The generic name *Cynodon* comes from the Greek κύνος (*kynos*), 'dog', and ὀδοντος (*odontos*), 'tooth', possibly from the rough spikelets. Its root was used as a diuretic and anti-inflammatory.

The name 'gramegna' in the annotation ('Gramigna' in Mattioli, pp. 1052–4) is still the common name in Italy for both species (*Cynodon dactylon* is known as 'gramigna' and *Poa pratensis* as 'gramigna dei prati').

470
fiori de gramegno
470

266. [?] Eulalia, *Miscanthus sinensis* Andersson

Windsor, RL 19405

287 x 266 mm. *Watermark*: Fleur de lys 52

NUMBERING: *471* (twice)

MOUNT SHEET: Type D

PROVENANCE: Sir Rex Nan Kivell

It is impossible to identify this plant with certainty on the basis of the illustration, but this may be Eulalia, a species belonging to the family Poaceae. The plant originally came from the temperate regions of east Asia (China, Japan, Korea, Taiwan), Indonesia and the Philippines, and is now naturalized all over the world and prized as an ornamental plant.

471
471

267. Creeping Jenny, *Lysimachia nummularia* L.

Windsor, RL 19406

255 x 225 mm. *Watermark*: Fleur de lys 50

NUMBERING: *478*

MOUNT SHEET: Type D

PROVENANCE: Sir Rex Nan Kivell

The creeping Jenny is a herbaceous perennial of the family Primulaceae, found throughout southern and eastern Europe and western Asia, along the banks of rivers and ditches and in damp meadows and forest clearings. It multiplies primarily by vegetative means, since its nodes are capable of sending down adventitious roots.

This illustration shows the plant in flower but without its roots. The stem is slender and brown with pairs of broad oval leaves arranged along its entire length. Growing on long petioles from the axils of the lower leaves are four flowers, each made up of five elliptical petals that come to sharp points; they are yellow spotted with brown, indicating the presence of glands.

The Greek name λυσιμάχιον (*lysimachion*) used by Dioscorides and Galen, and the Latin variant used by Pliny ('Lysimachia'), came from λύσις (*lysis*), 'loosening', and μάχη (*machi*), 'battle', i.e. 'the plant that ends strife', and denoted various plants of the genus *Lysimachia* or *Lythrum* (see **260**). Galen attributed tranquillizing properties to the plant and Pliny wrote that it could calm quarrels. *Lysimachia nummularia* and the related yellow loosestrife, *L. vulgaris*, were once cultivated for the astringent and relaxing properties of their roots.

478

268. Tormentil, *Potentilla reptans* L.

Windsor, RL 19407

281 x 258 mm

NUMBERING: *481*

MOUNT SHEET: Type D

PROVENANCE: Sir Rex Nan Kivell

This unfinished drawing shows the tormentil, a herbaceous perennial of the family Rosaceae. It is native to temperate regions of Europe and Asia and has become naturalized all over the world, growing in meadows, damp habitats and uncultivated areas at altitudes to 1,500m. The specimen has a slender, flexible stem and five palmate leaves (two drawn in outline only) growing from long petioles and made up of five elliptical lobes with bluntly toothed margins. Two flowers with rounded yellow obcordate petals grow on slender pedicels from their axils. In one blossom numerous stamens ending in dark anthers can be seen, while at the base of the other the calyx, consisting of long, narrow sepals, is visible.

The generic name of the plant comes from the Latin *potens*, 'powerful', because of the many healing virtues attributed to it. The common name tormentil derives from the Latin for intestinal colic, *tormina,* because the root was used to treat this complaint. Many sixteenth-century herbals cite it as a specific for dysentery and the plague, and it was also used in the treatment of tuberculosis. According to Mattioli (p. 1071), the leaves of the closely related 'Potentilla tormentilla' (now called *Potentilla erecta*), placed in the shoes or bound to the palms of one's hands, could reduce fever.

269. Salad burnet, *Sanguisorba minor* Scop.

Windsor, RL 19408
213 x 263 mm
NUMBERING: *485*
ANNOTATION: *Minore* ('Lesser')
MOUNT SHEET: Type D
PROVENANCE: Sir Rex Nan Kivell

The salad burnet is a herbaceous annual of the family Rosaceae, native to Europe, North Africa and temperate regions of Asia, and naturalized all over the world, growing in arid grassland and shrubland with calcareous soil at altitudes from sea level to 1,300m. The plant was once cultivated in kitchen gardens as a salad green, but today it is grown almost exclusively as forage. The upper part of the plant is shown, with its slender, flexible stem and alternate, feather-like leaves composed of seven or eight lanceolate leaflets with toothed margins and acute apices. The flowers are united in terminal inflorescences growing on long scapes from the axils of the leaves.

The salad burnet was originally classified by Linnaeus as *Poterium sanguisorba*, from the Greek ποτήριον (*poterion*), 'drinking cup', probably because of the cup-like form that the flower cluster assumes after it dries. Dioscorides had used the term for a fruticose plant, perhaps an astragalus. The epithet *sanguisorba*, from *sanguis* ('blood') and *sorbere* ('to draw off'), was given to the plant because of its haemostatic properties, although the related great burnet, *Sanguisorba officinalis*, was more commonly used. The annotation has been partly trimmed off, but probably referred to the illustration of the plant (as 'Pimpinella Minore') on p. 1088 of the *Discorsi*.

269

270. Soft rush, *Juncus effusus* L.

Windsor, RL 19409

414 x 268 mm

NUMBERING: *486* (twice)

ANNOTATION: *Giunco' e' di piu spetie. / il seme arostito, e' beuto / con vino inacquato. ristagna / il corpo. e' i flussi rossi / delle donne, provoca el / orina. e' fa dolore di testa / Le fronde tenere piu pro= / pinque alla radice. simpi= / astra utilmente a' i, morsi / di quei ragni che si chiamano / phalangi~~hi~~ il seme e' sonni= / fero. 1091* ('There are many species of rush. The seed, roasted and drunk in diluted wine, settles the body and staunches the menstrual flows of women. It stimulates urination and causes headaches. The tender leaves closest to the root are usefully applied to bites from those spiders that are called *phalangi*. The seed is sleep-inducing. 1091') [From Mattioli 1568, p. 1091]

PROVENANCE: Sir Rex Nan Kivell

This drawing illustrates a soft, nodeless rush with a basal sheath and a pseudolateral inflorescence, probably *Juncus effusus*. A cosmopolitan plant belonging to the family Juncaceae, it can be found growing in damp areas in all the temperate zones of the world. The stem of this specimen is erect with two brown basal sheaths and an anthela made up of numerous small flowers growing on peduncles from the axil of a bract that seems to be an extension of the stem. The genus name *Juncus* comes from the Latin *jungere*, 'to bind', as the flexible stems of these plants have since ancient times been woven into cords, mats, baskets and so on.

Cesi's annotation copies a passage from Dioscorides on p. 1091 of Mattioli's *Discorsi*, but the accompanying illustration on that page ('Giunco florido') actually depicts the hygrophilous flowering rush, *Butomus umbellatus*.

406
Giunco è di piu spetie.
il seme arostito. e beuto
con uino inacquato. ristagna
il corpo. e i flussi rossi
delle donne. prouoca el
orina. e fa dolore di testa
le fronde tenere piu pro=
pinque alla radice. s'impi=
astra utilmente a i morsi
di quei ragni che si chiamano
falangie il seme è sonni=
fero. 1091
486

271. Vallarsan lungwort, *Pulmonaria vallarsae* A. Kern.

Windsor, RL 19410

195 x 267 mm

NUMBERING: *487*

MOUNT SHEET: Type D

PROVENANCE: Sir Rex Nan Kivell

This species of lungwort is a herbaceous perennial belonging to the family Boraginaceae that grows almost exclusively in Italy, where it may be found in broadleaved forests of oak and beech at altitudes between 300m and 1,600m. It takes its name from the Val Vallarsa in Trentino–Alto Adige, where it was first recorded. The spots on the leaves of the lungwort were supposedly reminiscent of the spots on a tubercular lung (hence the generic name, from the Latin *pulmo*, lung), and following the doctrine of signatures the various species of lungwort were thus used to treat consumption.

The stem of this specimen is robust and covered with thick, erect hairs. The alternate, sessile leaves are elliptical with entire margins and acute apices. Large pale blue patches can be seen scattered across the upper sides of the leaf blades. The flowers grow in a scorpioid (coil-like) arrangement at the ends of long stems; they have brown calyxes, short petioles and light blue corollas with five rounded lobes. The stamens and pistils are not clearly shown.

487

272. Cockscomb, *Celosia argentea* L. var. *cristata* (L.) Kuntze cv.

Windsor, RL 19411

330 x 259 mm

NUMBERING: *491*

MOUNT SHEET: Type D

PROVENANCE: Sir Rex Nan Kivell

This drawing shows the inflorescence of a cultivar of the cockscomb, a herbaceous annual of the family Amaranthaceae native to tropical Asia. The erect, smooth stem ends in a capitulum made up of numerous deep red flowers with fringed edges.

The cockscomb was introduced to Europe as an ornamental during the second half of the sixteenth century. It was known to Cassiano's contemporaries as *amaranthus*, and was still popularly called an amaranth into the nineteenth century, though Linnaeus had proposed the distinct genus *Celosia* (from the Greek κηλός (*kelos*), 'dry' or 'burnt', for its colour) to separate it from *Amaranthus* because its flowers are unisex rather than hermaphrodite and its stamens are free rather than united in pairs at their base. The name *cristata* comes from the resemblance of the flower cluster to a cockscomb. This feature is accentuated in cultivated varieties in which horticulturists induced fasciation, the union of two or three flower stalks so that the crimson bracts with their flowers form a broad, flattened, brush-like cluster.

273. Unidentified plant

Windsor, RL 19412

249 x 212 mm

NUMBERING: *492*

MOUNT SHEET: Type D

PROVENANCE: Sir Rex Nan Kivell

This drawing is of a plant belonging to the family Asteraceae, although it cannot be more precisely identified. The stem is erect and slender, with alternate, sessile leaves, lanceolate with toothed or lobed margins. The capitulum is made up of a core of tubulose flowers surrounded by yellow peripheral ligulate flowers. The bracts of the head, a detail that might have helped to identify the plant, are not shown.

492

274. Vervain, *Verbena officinalis* L.

Private collection

424 x 269 mm

NUMBERING: *493* [twice]

ANNOTATION: *Verbenaca. Le fronde inco / rporate con grasso di porco / fresco, overo con olio rosato. e / poscia impiastrate. levano i, dolori / della madrice. impiastrate con aceto / spengono il fuoco sacro. e fermano / el ulcere putride e' corosive. salda / le ferite. Leva piu che ognialtra / cosa. il dolore del capo 1107* ('Vervain. The leaves, mixed with fresh pork fat or rose oil, are applied to relieve pains of the uterus. Applied with vinegar they extinguish holy fire [erysipelas] and stop putrid and corrosive ulcers. Heals wounds. Relieves headaches more than any other thing. 1107') [From Mattioli 1568, pp. 1106–8]

MOUNT SHEET: Type D

PROVENANCE: Boone sale, lot 139

LITERATURE: *Cassiano Segreti* 2000, cat. 89; *L'Uccelliera* 2000, fig. xvib, pp. 49, 116; *Cassiano Segreti* 2001, cat. 167

The vervain is a perennial herbaceous species belonging to the family Verbenaceae (see also **275**). Native to Europe and North America, it has become cosmopolitan, growing close to human habitations and along roadsides and paths at altitudes from sea level to 1,200m.

The whole plant is shown here. The stem is erect, slender and branching near its apex. The opposite leaves are ovate-lanceolate with lobed margins and clearly marked veins. The upper branches bear tiny pale violet flowers; in the detail at lower left, it can be seen that the corolla is divided into five lobes. The brown taproot bears a number of rootlets.

According to Varro (*De lingua latina* 5, 47), at new year Romans would exchange gifts of pots of vervain (*arbor felix*) gathered in a Sabine forest sacred to Strena, goddess of good fortune and happiness (Cattabiani 1996). Pliny counted it among the most precious of herbs, believing it to have great medicinal and magical powers, and reported a legend that it should be gathered with the left hand after drawing a circle around the plant with a sword. During the Middle Ages it was believed that the herb could protect against the plague. Savonarola cited vervain as an immaculate plant with purifying properties and recommended that it be eaten and followed by at least seven days of chastity.

493
Verbenaca. Le fronde inco
rporate con grasso di porco
fresco, ouero con olio rosato. e
poscia impiastrate. Leuano i dolori
della madrice. impiastrate con aceto
spengono il fuoco sacro. e fermano
l'ulcere putride. e corosiue. salda
le ferite. Leua piu che ogni altra
cosa. il dolore del capo. 1107
493

275. Vervain, *Verbena officinalis* L.

Windsor, RL 19413

369 x 261 mm

NUMBERING: *494*

ANNOTATION: *Unaltra verbenaca; herba di Sa*[*n*] *Giovanne* ('Another vervain. St John's herb')

MOUNT SHEET: Type D

PROVENANCE: Sir Rex Nan Kivell

The artist shows an entire vervain (see **274**) without its flowers. The stem is straight, thick and smooth. The leaves are alternate and lanceolate with short petioles and indented margins that are either toothed or lobed. The root system consists of a horizontal rhizome with branching rootlets. As noted at the foot of the page, vervain was one of the plants associated with St John the Baptist: traditionally, the night of the feast of St John (24 June, and thus close to the summer solstice) was the most propitious time to gather certain herbs that would be used in the course of the coming year for medicinal and ritual purposes, including vervain, St John's wort (**258**), mistletoe (**238**), elder and several others.

Verbena verbenaca.
Eerba di Sā Giouanne
494

276. Hyacinth, *Hyacinthus orientalis* L.

Windsor, RL 19414

369 x 261 mm. *Watermark*: Fleur de lys 53

NUMBERING: *497* (twice)

ANNOTATION: *Hiacintho, che scriuono / i poeti essere nato del sa= / ngue d'Aiace, dove si ritro= / vano ancora le lettere del / suo nome 1109.* ('Hyacinth, of which the poets write that it was born from the blood of Ajax, and in which the letters of his name can still be found. 1109.') [From Mattioli 1568, p. 1109]

MOUNT SHEET: Type D

PROVENANCE: Sir Rex Nan Kivell

LITERATURE: Freedberg 1989, pp. 47, 50 (fig. 11); *Quaderni Puteani* 4, pp. 198–9 (cat. 121); *Cassiano* cat. 1997, p. 32 (cat. 62)

The hyacinth is a bulbous herbaceous perennial of the family Hyacinthaceae; originally from the Near East, it is now cultivated and naturalized all over the world. It was introduced to Italy during the middle of the sixteenth century. Mattioli recounts that a specimen was sent to him from Padua by Giacomo Antonio Cortuso, who was to serve as *prefetto* of the city's botanical garden from 1590 to 1603.

The drawing shows an entire plant complete with its round bulb, whitish tunic and fasciculate roots. It has six linear leaves which are bent into a broad V along the blade's central furrow. The two scapes each carry four or five bell-shaped flowers, whose corollas are blue streaked with red and terminate in six long lobes. The stamens and the pistil are not visible.

In Greek mythology the birth of the flower was associated with the blood spilt by both Hyacinth, the youth beloved of Apollo and accidentally slain by him in a game of discus, and Ajax, the Homeric hero who killed himself from shame after having slaughtered a group of sheep (mistaken in a fit of mad rage for Trojans and for Odysseus, who had been awarded Achilles' armour in his stead). The letters 'Ai' were said to be imprinted on the leaves of the flower, interpreted as the first letters of Ajax's name (as noted in the annotation) or as Apollo's lament ('ai ai' being Greek for 'alas' or 'woe').

The annotation refers to p. 1109 of Mattioli's *Discorsi*, although the illustration on that page (captioned 'Hiacintho') shows a tassel hyacinth, *Leopoldia comosa*, a species quite different from the plant shown here. A hyacinth instead appears on p. 1110 ('Hiacintho orientale').

497
Hiacintho, che scriuono
i poeti essere nato del sa=
ngue d'Aiace, doue si rico=
nosco ancora le lettere del
suo nome. 1109.
497

277. Alpine squill, *Scilla bifolia* L.

Windsor, RL 19415

182 x 239 mm. *Watermark*: Eagle in circle with indistinct surmounting element (cut)

NUMBERING: *498*

MOUNT SHEET: Type D

PROVENANCE: Sir Rex Nan Kivell

The Alpine squill is a bulbous herbaceous perennial of the family Hyacinthaceae that is common all over Europe (except the far north) and western Asia, growing in broadleaved forests at altitudes from 500m to 2,000m, and cultivated as an ornamental.

The plant has two linear leaves with pointed tips. The floral scape, which is reddish in colour and slightly longer than the leaves, divides in two at its distal end and terminates in two flowers. These are deep blue in colour with six tepals, dark stamens and blue anthers. The bulb and roots of the plant are not shown.

Ancient authors including Theophrastus, Pliny and Dioscorides used the term *scilla* to refer to the sea onion, *Urginea maritima*, a plant which has recently been transferred to the genus *Charybdis*; that species is still valued for its medicinal properties, whereas *Scilla bifolia* has no such use. The word *scilla* derives from the Greek σκέλλω (*skello*), 'to dry or drain', as the plant can survive in dry climates.

498

OTHER DAL POZZO BOTANICAL DRAWINGS

The following sixteen drawings are not *en suite* with the material in the *Erbario Miniato*, and appear for the most part to have been produced several decades later, for either Cassiano dal Pozzo or his brother, Carlo Antonio. The 'Pozzo' numbering found on several of the sheets overlaps with that of the *Erbario* sequence, and suggests that they were considered as a separate sequence from the *Erbario*. The anthropomorphic apple (**280**), for example, is numbered *388*, a number also assigned to the lily of the valley (**243–244**) in the *Erbario* sequence. The numbering *388* indicates that the apple was placed close to the anomalous pineapple (**279**), numbered *382*. The next extant plant drawing in this 'Pozzo' number sequence is the twinned melon (**281**), numbered *426*; while this may suggest that Cassiano owned fifty or more depictions of anomalous fruit and vegetables – perhaps also including the broccoli (**291**), which has lost its 'Pozzo' number – our understanding of the 'Pozzo' numbering is still incomplete, and such speculations are of limited value. The same sequence may, for example, have included non-plant specimens such as the polished stones depicted on another drawing in the Paper Museum, numbered *394* and *395* (Windsor, RL 25490, forthcoming Part B.IX).

278 to **288** are catalogued here in the order of their 'Pozzo' numbers, with the unnumbered sheets following.

278. Pear, *Pyrus communis* L.

Private collection

229 x 142 mm

NUMBERING: *216*

MOUNT SHEET: Type D

PROVENANCE: Boone sale, lot 146

The pear is a tree of the family Rosaceae whose wild ancestors were probably native to Eurasia. It was not known to the peoples of ancient Egypt and Mesopotamia, and first appeared in Greece and Italy during antiquity. It does not exist in spontaneous form and is considered to represent a complex of hybrids between *Pyrus pyraster* and *Pyrus nivalis* or other species not present in Italy, which have been stabilized by cultivation. The diversity of early names for the pear may suggest that its cultivation sprang up independently in different sites. We find it called ἄπιος (*apios*) by Theophrastus and Aristotle, and ὄγχνη or ὄχνη (*ochne*) by Homer and Theocritus. In the works of Pliny, Virgil and Horace it appears under the Latin name *pirus* or *pirum*.

This drawing appears to depict a rare variety of pear similar to that known in Italy as 'butirra d'Amanlis striata' (and in France as 'beurré d'Amanlis panachée'). The two fruits in the upper part of the page have furrows along their length that give a lobed, segmented appearance. They are attached by long stems to a short shoot covered in rough bark and bearing four leaves. The leaves are heart-shaped with long petioles, acute apices and finely toothed margins. Below are a cross-section, showing five carpel cavities containing the seeds, and a longitudinal section in which the point of contact between the calyx and the true fruit can be seen, marked by two fine yellow lines in the pulp.

216

279. Pineapple, *Ananas comosus* (L.) Merr.

Attr. VINCENZO LEONARDI (*fl.* 1621–46)

Windsor, RL 28738

381 x 284 mm

NUMBERING: *382*

MOUNT SHEET: Type D

PROVENANCE: Boone sale, lot 144

LITERATURE: *Quaderni Puteani* 4, p. 190 (cat. 115); *Cassiano* cat. 1997, p. 31 (cat. 55)

The pineapple is a herbaceous species of the family Bromeliaceae. Native to southern Brazil and Paraguay, it had spread as far as the Caribbean when it was discovered by Christopher Columbus on the island of Guadeloupe. It was introduced to Europe and grown under glass, and today it is cultivated in all the tropical regions of the world. The pineapple was one of the first exotic fruits from the New World to be documented by travellers (as in Ramusio 1556, III, pl. 136, and Thevet 1575, II). A copy of Ligozzi's drawing of the pineapple (Uffizi, 1931 Orn.) was given by the Grand Duke of Tuscany, Ferdinando I de' Medici, to Aldrovandi in 1591 (Bologna, BU, MS Aldrovandi, *Tavole* vol. 3, *Piante fiori frutta*, fol. 196).

The drawing shows a fruit that has been deformed either by disease or genetic mutation, for it has not only a rosette of leaves at its apex, but also a thick cluster of leaves at its base. The stem is robust and bears two long, linear leaves with finely toothed margins and pointed tips. The clusters of leaves are shorter, but also linear and finely toothed. The fruit is a syncarp of numerous berries, bearing scales with long sharp points.

The drawing is one of the few botanical studies from Cassiano's collection that can be attributed to his artist-collaborator Vincenzo Leonardi (pp. 15–16 and 36; see also **280, 281** and **292**).

280. Apple, *Malus pumila* Mill.

Attr. VINCENZO LEONARDI (*fl.* 1621–46)

Windsor, RL 32569

151 x 113 mm

NUMBERING: *388*

MOUNT SHEET: Type D

PROVENANCE: Cyril Fry; Dudley Snelgrove; from whose heirs purchased in 1993

LITERATURE: *Quaderni Puteani* 4, pp. 147, 219, 221 (cat. 140); *Cassiano* cat. 1997, p. 34 (cat. 76); Freedberg 2002, pp. 355, 405–6 (fig. 14.1)

The subject of this drawing has been variously identified as a pear (Freedberg in *Quaderni Puteani* 4, p. 147), a dried fruit 'of Central or South American origin' (Solinas in *idem*, p. 219), a coconut (McBurney in *Cassiano* cat. 1997, p. 34), and a dried calabash, apple or coconut (Freedberg 2002, p. 405). It is most probably an apple (see **287**) – the colour and shape suggests the pearmain cultivar, grown in Europe since the Middle Ages – affected by scab, an air-borne fungus that commonly attacks apples and pears. The yellow haloes around the 'eyes' and the puckering of the skin are characteristic of fruit attacked by these pathogens.

The anthropomorphic features were doubtless emphasized (whether consciously or not) by the artist, probably Vincenzo Leonardi (see **279**). This apple would have been appreciated as a *lusus naturae*, a 'joke of nature' of a type fashionable among collectors and in cabinets of curiosity at this time. The concept of the 'playfulness' of nature had its origins in Aristotle, Ovid and Pliny, and it was Pliny's notion of *natura pictrix* ('nature the painter') that best described for seventeenth-century naturalists such images made by chance, examples of 'nature's ability to be both artist and canvas' (Findlen 1990, p. 297). 'Nature jokes with art', noted Lodovico Moscardo (a contemporary of the dal Pozzo brothers in Verona) of a curious stone in his museum, 'since in it she reveals many lines that form the shapes of trees, houses and countrysides, as if the learned hand of some famous painter had sketched them' (Moscardo 1651, p. 148). 'Thus Nature has joked, imprinting a human figure', remarked the Jesuit scientist Gaspar Schott on seeing an anthropomorphic orchid in the collection of the Collegio Romano (Schott 1697, p. 1362). But nature's creativity was matched by man's imagination or intervention in such unlikely 'specimens' as the fruit in the shape of a human face depicted hanging from its twig in the museum of the Veronese apothecary Francesco Calzolari (1521–1600) (comp. fig. 280), or the piece of apple bark in the form of a human face illustrated in Aldrovandi's *Dendrologia* (1668; illustrated in Freedberg 2002, p. 406). The perception of images, especially of holy figures, in the random patterns of fish scales, stains on walls, burnt toast and so on remains a common phenomenon to this day.

Comp. fig. 280. Interior of Francesco Calzolari's museum in Verona (detail). B. Ceruti and A. Chiocco, *Museum Francisci Calceolarii*, Verona 1622

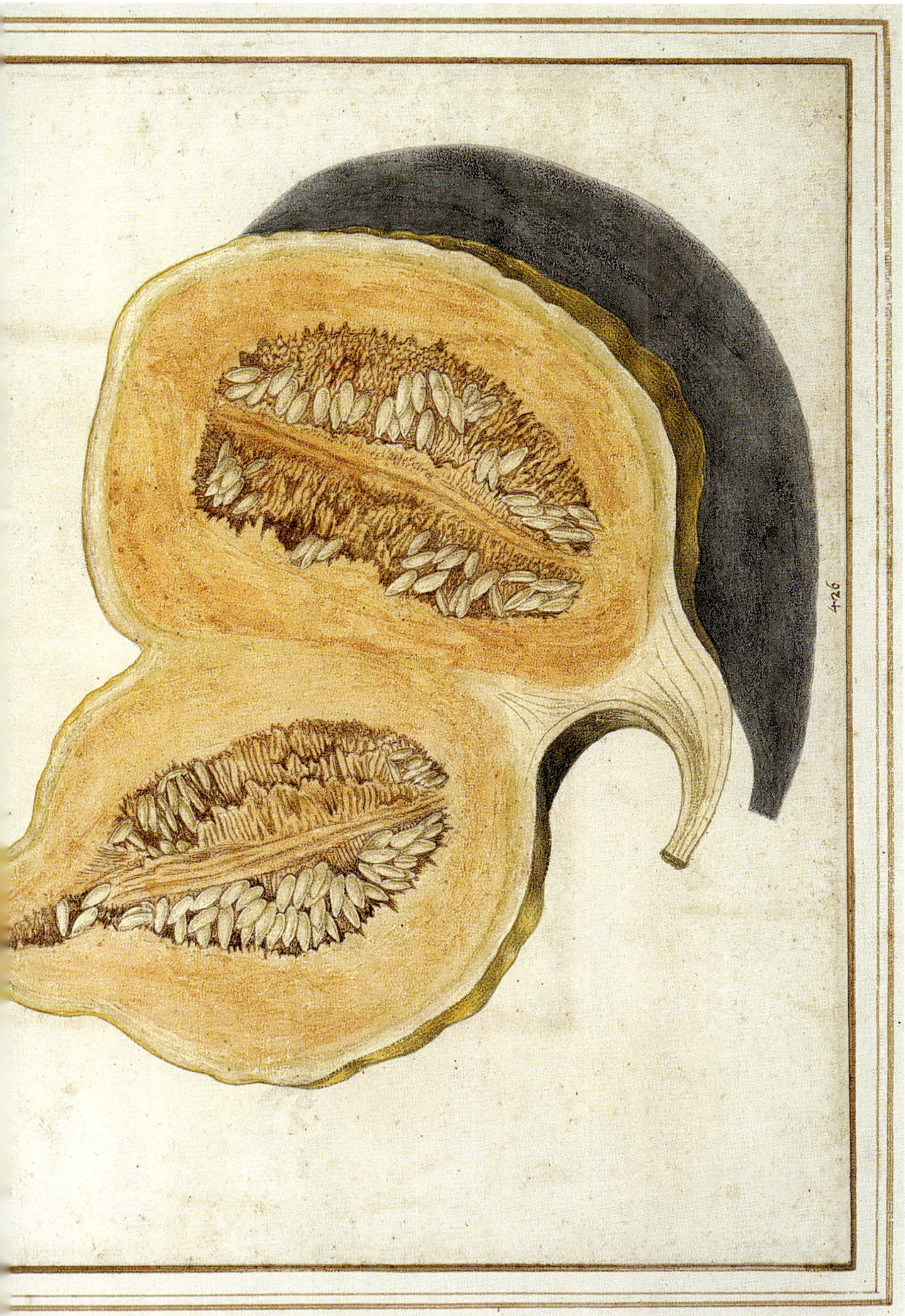
426

281. Melon, *Cucumis melo* L.

Attr. VINCENZO LEONARDI (*fl.* 1621–46)
Windsor, RL 19365
532 x 348 mm
NUMBERING: *426*
MOUNT SHEET: Type D
PROVENANCE: Sir Rex Nan Kivell
LITERATURE: *Cassiano* cat. 1997, p. 31 (cat. 56); *Amazing Rare Things* 2007, pp. 96, 98 (pl. 32)

This work portrays a deformed specimen of the melon, *Cucumis melo*, a herbaceous annual of the family Cucurbitaceae (see also **290**). The plant is native to parts of Africa, eastern Asia, Australia and various Pacific islands, and is now cultivated and naturalized in all tropical areas of the world. Paintings from Herculaneum demonstrate that the melon was being cultivated in Italy in Roman times, and Pliny noted that the Emperor Tiberius was fond of the fruit.

The specimen illustrated here is a single fruit that has developed abnormally, probably as a result of two ovaries on the same flower having developed simultaneously after pollination. Its rough yellow rind bears a characteristic network pattern, as it belongs to the 'reticulate' group of the species. The longitudinal section shows the dense orange pulp and numerous flat whitish seeds.

282. Medlar, *Mespilus germanica* L.

Arader Galleries, New York
506 x 347 mm. *Watermark*: Figure 58c
NUMBERING: *523*
MOUNT SHEET: Type D
PROVENANCE: Boone sale, lot 154

This fruiting branch may tentatively be identified as a medlar, a tree of the family Rosaceae that is common in southern and eastern Europe in forests in mountainous areas, and is cultivated and naturalized all over the world. This illustration shows a woody branch bearing smooth yellow fruit and leaves on short petioles. The ovate blades have entire margins and apices that end in a small mucro.

Theophrastus called this fruit tree (and oriental whitethorn species believed to be related to it) μεσπίλη (*mespile*), from which came the Latin *mespilum* and thence the Italian 'nespolo'. When the Romans conquered Britain they found the tree already being cultivated there. The fruits are sour at maturity, and must be stored in a dry place until they begin to decompose, whereupon they are sweet enough to eat. The medlar was valued as a source of winter fruit, and as the basis for remedies against diarrhoea and other digestive problems. It remained a popular fruit until the late eighteenth century, since when it has fallen from favour.

282

283. Cedar of Lebanon, *Cedrus libani* A. Rich. 1823

Private collection

368 x 216 mm. *Watermark*: Figure 15

NUMBERING: *562*; *563*

MOUNT SHEET: Type D

PROVENANCE: Boone sale, lot 137

The drawing illustrates the female and male cones of the cedar of Lebanon, a tree of the family Pinaceae that is native to Lebanon, Turkey and Cyprus. The female cone, above, is oval in form and made up of numerous broad, overlapping scales. It is attached by a short, curved, woody stem to a twig bearing needle-like leaves arranged in two verticils. Below is the male cone, consisting of a central axis from which hundreds of stamens have fallen away. Their points of insertion, arranged in a compact spiral, can clearly be seen.

The cedar of Lebanon has been known and admired since antiquity, and is mentioned in the writings of many classical authors. According to Vitruvius the celebrated statue of Diana of Ephesus was made of cedar wood, while Theophrastus stated that the temples of Asia were entirely covered with panels of this wood; Solomon supposedly used its timber to construct the Temple of Jerusalem. Many classical references are ambiguous, however, since juniper wood was also referred to as cedar wood (Meiggs 1982, pp. 410–16). The cedar of Lebanon was reintroduced to western European gardens in the sixteenth century, and is described and illustrated in Mattioli's *Discorsi* (1568) on p. 140 (as 'Cedrus maggiore del Monte Libano').

562
563

284. Globe artichoke, *Cynara scolymus* L.

Private collection

Two sheets joined horizontally at centre: upper sheet 204 x 179 mm; lower sheet 206 x 179 mm

NUMBERING: *598; 599*

This unusual specimen of a globe artichoke (see **222**) has two heads growing from a single stem. The stalk is erect and ribbed and carries at its apex a pair of still-closed flower heads. The scales of the involucres are oval with deeply notched apices. Below, on a separate piece of paper, is a longitudinal section of the same specimen, in which can be seen the layered arrangement of the scales and the receptacles where the flowers are inserted.

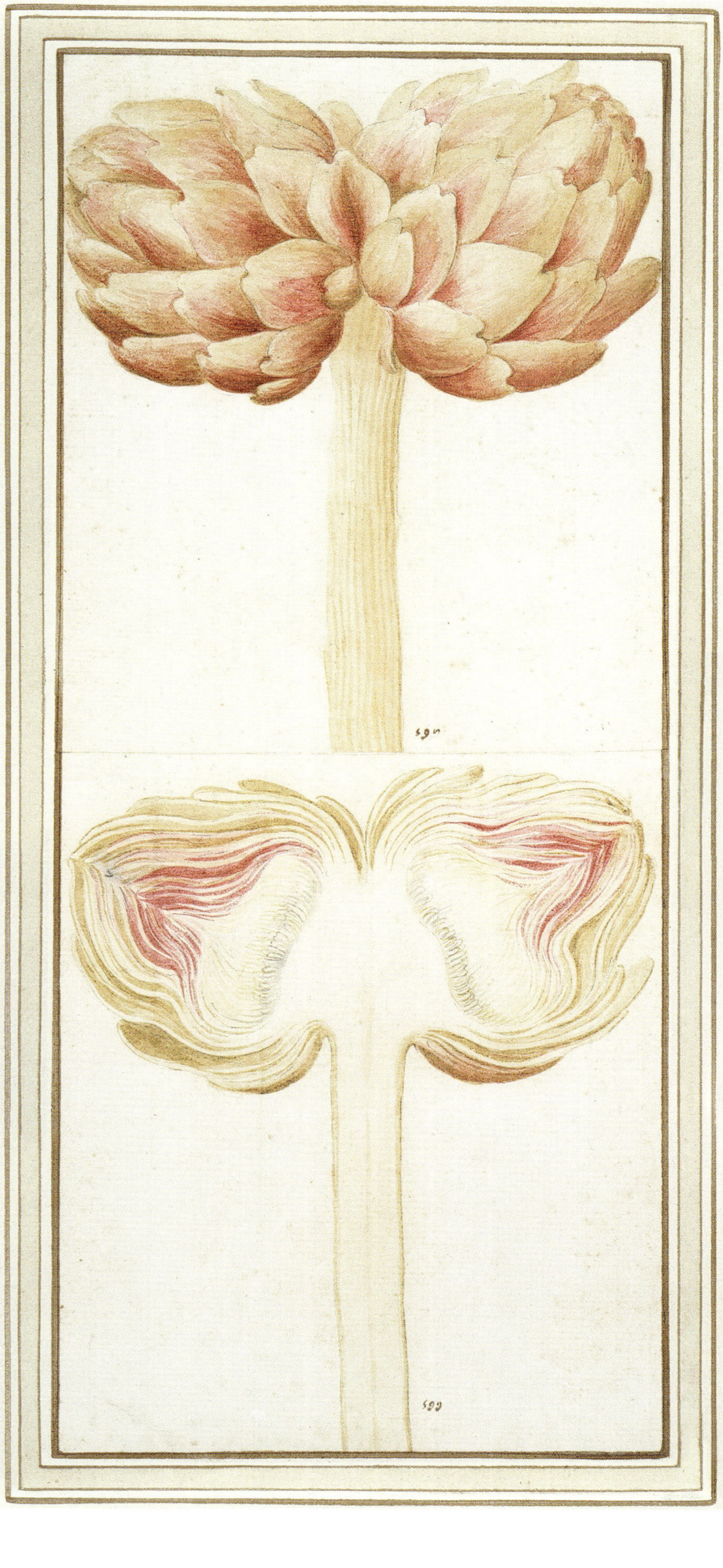

284

603

285. Red cabbage, *Brassica oleracea* L. var. *capitata* c.v. 'Rubra'

Private collection

406 x 553 mm. *Watermark*: Crown with star

NUMBERING: *603*

PROVENANCE: Robert de Belder, Belgium; Kate de Rothschild, UK

The red cabbage is a cultivar of *Brassica oleracea* (see **286**; also **291**), a herbaceous species belonging to the family Brassicaceae or Cruciferae that has been cultivated since prehistoric times and exists in many different forms. All the European cabbages (including kales, broccolis, kohlrabi, sprouts and so on) belong to the species *Brassica oleracea*, which is subdivided into many groups, the 'true' cabbages and savoys all belonging to the *capitata* group. The Latin *brassica*, found for example in the writings of Pliny and Cato, may derive from a Celtic word *bresic*, as the Romans may have discovered the cabbage (and adopted its name) during their conquest of central Europe. For centuries there was a popular belief that the cabbage was noxious, a statement that was repeated by Theophrastus, Pliny and Mattioli.

In this drawing the artist shows the plant from above to emphasize its rosette of broad leaves, with their rippled surfaces and irregular margins. The outer leaves are green, while the inner leaves are purplish-red. The following drawing presents a cross-section of the same species.

286. Red cabbage, *Brassica oleracea* L. var. *capitata* c.v. 'Rubra'

Private collection

292 x 283 mm

NUMBERING: *604*

PROVENANCE: Robert de Belder, Belgium; Kate de Rothschild, UK

The artist shows here the cross-section of a red cabbage (possibly the same specimen as **285**), showing the thick stem with dark red leaves growing in close alternation.

286

287. Apple, *Malus pumila* Mill.

Private collection

232 x 192 mm

NUMBERING: *801*

MOUNT SHEET: Type D

PROVENANCE: Boone sale, lot 140

The apple is a tree of the family Rosaceae that is cultivated all over the world in a variety of climates and may be found growing spontaneously. Carbonized remains of the fruit have been found at Neolithic and Bronze Age sites in Europe, cut into halves and quarters, suggesting that they had been dried and stored for the winter. The apple was being cultivated in Egypt and Asia Minor by the thirteenth or twelfth century BC; the fruit is mentioned in Greek texts from the sixth century BC, and Pliny cites thirty-six different varieties of the apple. The Italian *mela* comes from the Latin *malum*, whereas the English name may be based on an Indo-European root *abel*. It has recently been convincingly argued that the correct scientific name for orchard apples, if *Malus* is to be maintained as a distinct genus, is *Malus pumila* Mill. rather than the more commonly applied *Malus domestica* Borkh. (Mabberley *et al*. 2001).

The fruit shown here is of the variety *Apiola stellata*, commonly called *mela pentagona* ('pentagonal apple'), an ancient cultivar that is still grown in the provinces of Veneto and Emilia Romagna. The fruit is of medium size, costate and slightly squat in profile; its five longitudinal lobes can be seen in the upper drawing. The smooth peel is yellowish-green with a red blush in the areas that were most exposed to the sun during maturation.

288. Cashew, *Anacardium occidentale* L.

Windsor, RL 19375

242 x 166 mm

NUMBERING: *984*

MOUNT SHEET: Type D

PROVENANCE: Sir Rex Nan Kivell

The cashew is a tree of the family Anacardiaceae. Originally from South America, it is now cultivated in tropical regions around the world. When it was introduced to Europe, this exotic plant immediately attracted the curiosity of naturalists and artists. Ligozzi drew a branch of the cashew tree weighed down with fruit (Uffizi, 1902 Orn.), which was reproduced with slight variations in a drawing made for Aldrovandi (Bologna, BU, MS Aldrovandi, *Tavole*, vol. 2, *Piante*, fol. 306).

The generic name *Anacardium* refers to the vaguely heart-shaped form of what was believed to be the fruit of the plant. However, this is instead the floral peduncle which swells into a pear-shaped protuberance, reddish or yellow in colour and known as the 'cashew apple'. The fleshy peduncle is depicted here, yellowish-white in colour, elongated and pear-shaped with a smooth surface. Externally it is divided into three long, asymmetrical lobes. The longitudinal cross-section is also asymmetrical and traversed by a darker structure that may represent a vascular bundle. The true fruit, a long, dark green, kidney-shaped nut partially embedded in the calyx at the end of the peduncle, is not shown. The nut has a hard pericarp covered with a thin outer shell; between the two is a cavity containing a resinous juice that blisters the skin and can be used as a lubricant and insecticide. The oily seed is the familiar 'cashew nut'; the fleshy portion is also edible when mature, and its juice is used in the production of wine and brandy in Brazil.

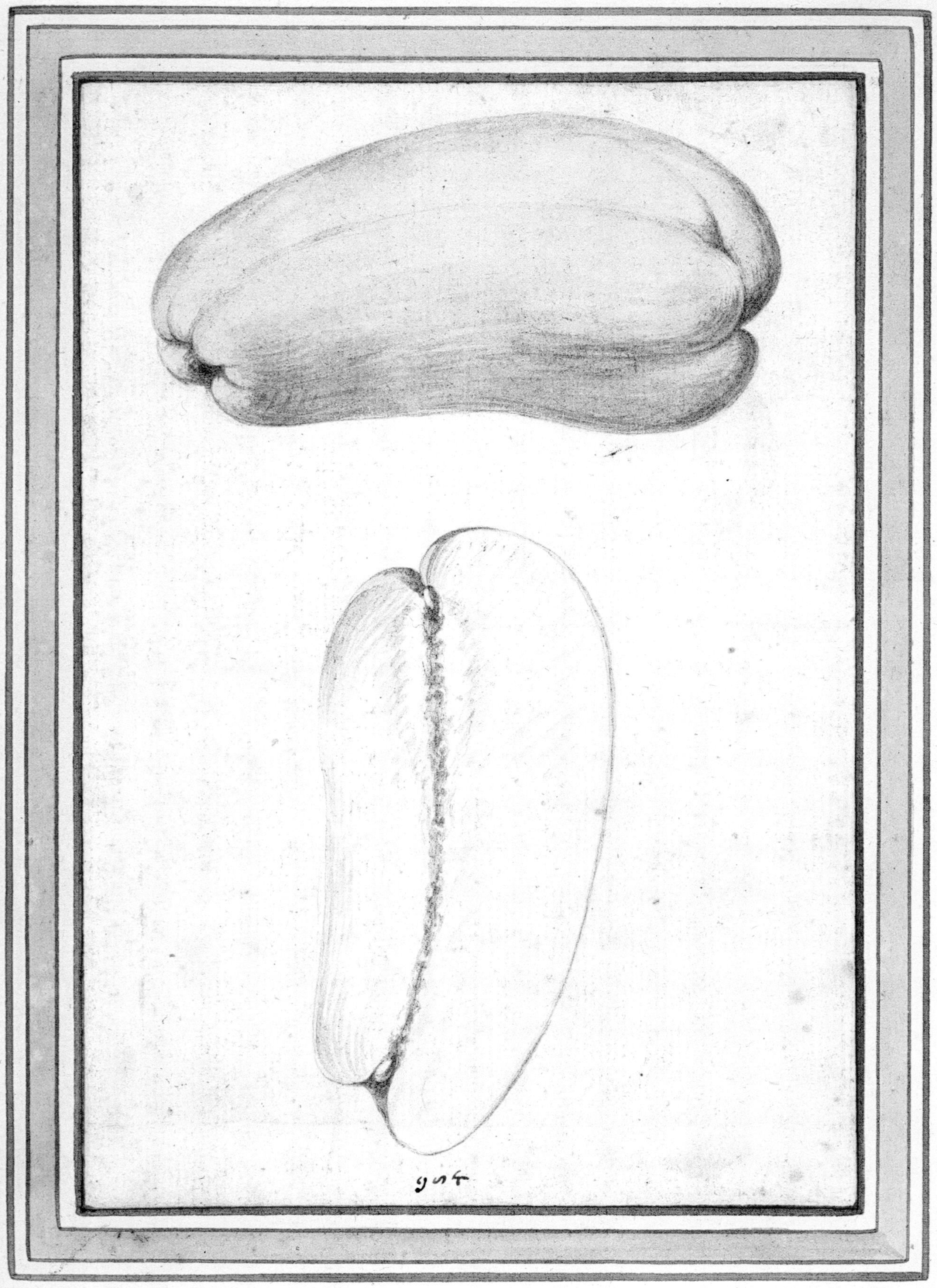

288

289. Thorn apple, *Datura stramonium* L.

Private collection (courtesy of England & Co Gallery, London)

279 x 312 mm

MOUNT SHEET: Type D

LITERATURE: *Quaderni Puteani* 4, p. 191 (cat. 116)

Here the artist has depicted an entire plant of the thorn apple, a herbaceous annual of the family Solanaceae, native to central America and introduced to Europe in the sixteenth century. It is now naturalized throughout the world, growing in open terrain to an altitude of 900m. The stem is erect and branching; the leaves, which grow from robust petioles, are oval in shape with deeply toothed margins and dark, prominent veins. At the apex of the branches the fruit can be seen – large capsules composed of four ovate valves covered with spines.

The white flower of the thorn apple is shrivelled and closed during the day, opening at night to emit an unpleasant odour. For this reason it was called *erba puzzola* or the 'stinking plant', while the fruit with its spiny capsule gave rise to the name *mela del diavolo* (devil's apple). The plant contains poisonous alkaloids which can cause psychological reactions and may affect the heart and respiration with fatal consequences. The hallucinogenic powers of the plant were known to the shamans of the Andes, and it has been suggested that some of the alleged phenomena of witchcraft were illusions induced by using *stramonium* ointments. Preparations made from the thorn apple – for example, its leaves mixed with pipe tobacco – have been used to treat asthma. It has been tested for the treatment of the trembling that is the main symptom of Parkinson's disease, but with little success.

289

290. Melon, *Cucumis melo* L.

Windsor, RL 19384
177 x 247 mm
MOUNT SHEET: Type D
PROVENANCE: Sir Rex Nan Kivell

This drawing shows a melon (see **281**) cut open to expose the mesocarp. The fruit is oval in shape with a rough rind ending in a small mucro at the distal end. The pulp is dense, varying in colour, and the cavity is filled with cream-coloured elliptical seeds.

291. Broccoli, *Brassica oleracea* L. var. *italica* Plenck

Windsor, RL 21143
343 x 464 mm
MOUNT SHEET: Type D
PROVENANCE: Sir Rex Nan Kivell
LITERATURE: *Quaderni Puteani* 4, p. 197 (cat. 120); *Cassiano* cat. 1997, pp. 31–2 (cat. 59); *Amazing Rare Things* 2007, p. 103 (pl. 36)

Like the cabbage (**285–286**), the broccoli is a cultivar of *Brassica oleracea*, a herbaceous species belonging to the family Brassicaceae. There has been considerable confusion over the vocabulary of the brassicas. The word broccoli has generally been used for those forms of cauliflower which do not produce heads until the year after sowing; but there are some varieties that have long been called broccoli despite producing heads in the autumn after sowing. Broccoli were often illustrated in botanical texts, and no fewer than sixteen varieties appear in Tabernaemontanus's *Eicones plantarum* (1590). Broccoli had long been cultivated in Italy when it was introduced to England in the early eighteenth century, and the few varieties then grown carried Italian names, Roman (purple-headed) and Neapolitan (white-headed).

This anomalous specimen has an enlarged and flattened stem, which carries at its top numerous green floral buds. The leaves, which are irregularly attached to the stem, vary from oval to lanceolate with toothed margins and rounded tips.

290

292. Pumpkin, *Cucurbita maxima* Duchesne

Attr. VINCENZO LEONARDI (*fl.* 1621–46)

Present location unknown

410 x 303 mm

MOUNT SHEET: Type D

PROVENANCE: Redfern Gallery, London; Sigmund Politzer (1946); Sotheby's (London), 10 July 2002, lot 152

The pumpkin is a herbaceous annual of the family Cucurbitaceae, originally from South America (Argentina and Uruguay). It has been cultivated in the Americas for thousands of years, and remains of the plant have been found at prehistoric sites in the south-western United States. It was cultivated in Europe after the discovery of the Americas, though the Greeks and Romans had a congenerous species, perhaps *Cucurbita moschata* (*zucca corta* or 'short pumpkin'). The seeds of *Cucurbita maxima* contain many active principles and can be used to expel tapeworms.

This drawing illustrates the cultivar sometimes referred to as *Cucurbita mixta*, having a spherical fruit with a thick, warty rind and deep narrow channels that divide its surface into longitudinal segments.

293. Globe artichoke, *Cynara scolymus* L.

Windsor, RL 26526

Pen and ink over black chalk

239 x 199 mm

ANNOTATION: *Carciofo mostruoso in forma di corno di douitia, simile alla figura / del cardo mostruoso; che mette Ferrante Imperati nella sua Hist*[*ori*]*:*[a] ('Monstrous artichoke in the form of a horn of plenty, similar to the illustration of the monstrous cardoon that Ferrante Imperato includes in his *History*')

MOUNT SHEET: Type D

PROVENANCE: Sir Rex Nan Kivell; Anthony Blunt

LITERATURE: *Quaderni Puteani* 4, p. 196 (cat. 119); *Cassiano* cat. 1997, p. 31 (cat. 57)

This pen-and-ink drawing shows a deformed artichoke (see **222–226** and **284**) with a broadened and flattened stem bearing several narrow, lanceolate leaves with short petioles, entire margins and sharp tips. The stem terminates in an immature inflorescence; around its base are rings of small, scale-like bracts with indented borders and spineless apices. At the base of the flower head are two degenerated capitulums.

The medium of pen and ink is unusual for the botanical illustrations in the Paper Museum (but cf. **242a**). The drawing is, however, similar in technique and style to many geological drawings in the collection inherited from Cesi, and it may be by the same (unidentified) artist as those sheets (see Part B.III, *Fossil Woods and other Geological Specimens*).

The note refers to the illustration of a 'Cardo Mostruoso a forma di Cornucopia' ('monstrous cardoon in the form of a cornucopia') in *Dell'historia naturale* by Ferrante Imperato (comp. fig. 293), a close friend of Cesi's and other members of the Accademia dei Lincei. A reference to this plate ('cardo mostruoso di Imperato') had also been included by Cesi in the sixth of his *Tabulae Phytosophicae* (see p. 39 and Fig. 17, p. 41).

Comp. fig. 293. Carline thistle (*Carlina vulgaris*). F. Imperato, *Dell'historia naturale*, Naples 1599, p. 760

Carciofo mostruoso in forma di corno di douitia, simile alla figura
del cardo mostruoso; che mette Ferrante Imperati nella sua Hist.

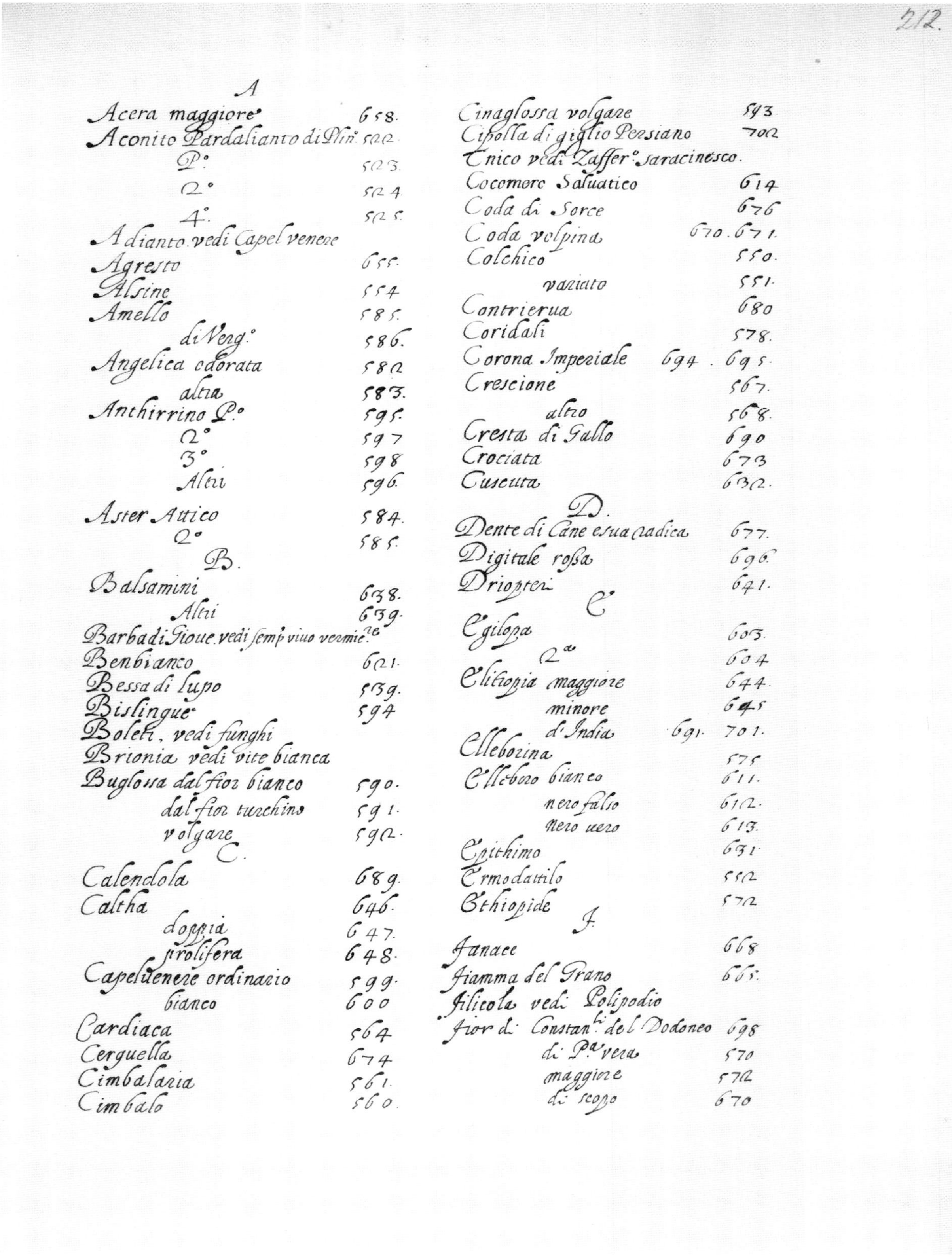
212.

A
Acera maggiore 658.
Aconito Pardalianto di Plin. 522.
P.° 523.
2.° 524.
4.° 525.
Adianto vedi Capel venere
Agresto 655.
Alsine 554
Amello 585.
di Verg.° 586.
Angelica odorata 582
altra 583.
Anthirrino P.° 595.
2.° 597
3.° 598
Altri 596.
Aster Attico 584.
2.° 585.
B.
Balsamini 638.
Altri 639.
Barba di Gioue vedi semp. viuo vermic.le
Benbianco 621.
Bessa di lupo 539.
Bislingue 594
Boleti, vedi funghi
Brionia vedi vite bianca
Buglossa dal fior bianco 590.
dal fior turchino 591.
volgare 592.
C.
Calendola 689.
Caltha 646.
doppia 647.
prolifera 648.
Capeluenere ordinario 599.
bianco 600
Cardiaca 564
Cerguella 674
Cimbalaria 561.
Cimbalo 560.
Cinaglossa volgare 543
Cipolla di giglio Persiano 702
Cnico vedi Zaffer.° saracinesco.
Cocomero Saluatico 614
Coda di Sorce 676
Coda volpina 670. 671.
Colchico 550.
variato 551.
Contrierua 680
Coridali 578.
Corona Imperiale 694. 695.
Crescione 567.
altro 568.
Cresta di Gallo 690
Crociata 673
Cuscuta 632.
D.
Dente di Cane e sua radica 677.
Digitale rossa 696.
Driopteri 641.
E
Egilopa 603.
2.a 604
Elitropia maggiore 644.
minore 645
d'India 691. 701.
Elleborina 575
Elleboro bianco 611.
nero falso 612.
nero uero 613.
Epithimo 631
Ermodattilo 552
Ethiopide 572
F.
Fanace 668
Fiamma del Grano 665.
Filicola vedi Polipodio
Fior di Constan.li del Dodoneo 698
di P.a vera 570
maggiore 572
di scoppo 670

Fig. 23. First index sheet of the *Erbario Miniato*, folio 212

Seventeenth-century indexes to the *Erbario Miniato*

At the end of the *Erbario Miniato* album are four sheets carrying two indexes: one alphabetical by plant name (fols 212–213; see Fig. 23) and the other by 'Pozzo' number (fols 214–215) – the small inked number found at upper centre of most drawings (see pp. 14 and 35). These indexes were probably compiled in Cassiano's household not long after the manuscript entered his collection in 1633, but are not in the usual 'scribal' hand found on most of the indexes to Cassiano's albums (see pp. 13–14). Nonetheless, the watermarks found on two of these sheets are of a type also found on other drawings in the Paper Museum that probably date to the 1630s or 1640s (see p. 618).

The names in the indexes are based on (though not always identical to) the inscriptions found on the drawing sheets. The numbers in the second column are 'Pozzo' numbers; the occasional scribal error is corrected in square brackets. The third column here provides the corresponding catalogue number.

Drawings bearing no inscriptions are not generally entered in the index. The typographical convention [–] has been used to indicate where the indexed name or number does not feature on the drawing itself; the name may have been added by the indexer on his own initiative or have been copied from inscriptions originally present on the sheets before they were trimmed during binding. Notable instances are *orecchia di lepre* ('hare's ear') for the caterpillar plant on **155**; *Radica di China* ('Chinese root') for the Chinese rhubarb on **160**; *Acera maggiore* for holly on **161**; *Isapi* (?) for a member of the mint family on **171**; and *Viola a ciocca semplice* for the hoary stock on **192** (*violacciocca* being an Italian common name for *Matthiola* sp.).

The indexer occasionally provides alternative names to those used in the inscriptions (which are mostly drawn from Dioscorides or Mattioli), supplanting them with common names used in Rome. Examples are *Porcacchia* rather than *Semprevivo minore* for **59** (*Sedum* spp.); *Marignani* rather than *Melanzane* for **21–22** (aubergines); *Suocer e Nuora* ('mother- and daughter-in-law') rather than *Iacea* for **91–92** (*Viola* spp.); and *Herba del papagallo* rather than *Herba maraviglia* for **173** (*Amaranthus tricolor*).

I. Alphabetical index

[*fol. 212*]

A

Acera maggiore	658.	**162**
Aconito Pardalianto di Plin^{o}.	522.	**24**
P.^{o}	523.	**25**
2 ^{o}	524.	**26**
4.º	525.	**27**
Adianto. vedi Capel venere		
Agresto	655.	**159**
Alsine	554	**56**
Amello	585.	**88**
di Verg.^{o}	586.	**89**
Angelica odorata	582	**85**
altra	583.	**86**
Anthirrino P.^{o}	595.	**98**
2°	597	**100**
3°	598	**101**
Altri	596.	**99**
Aster Attico	584.	**87**
2°	585.	**88**

B

Balsamini	638.	**141**
Altri	639.	**142**
Barba di Giove. vedi Semp'vivo vermic.^{re}		
Ben bianco	621.	**124**
Bessa di lupo	539.	**41**
Bislingue	594	**97**
Boleti, vedi funghi		
Brionia vedi vite bianca		
Buglossa dal fior bianco	590.	**93**
dal fior turchino	591.	**94**
volgare	592.	**95**

C

Calendola	689.	**193**
Caltha	646.	**149**
doppia	647.	**150**
prolifera	648.	**151**
Capelvenere ordinario	599.	**102**
bianco	600	**103**
Cardiaca	564	**66**
Cerquella	674	**178**
Cimbalaria	561.	**63**
Cimbalo	560.	**62**
Cinaglossa volgare	593.	**96**
Cipolla di giglio Persiano	702	**207**

Miriophillo. vedi. sop.^{ra} ciglio di Venere		
Mirride	581.	**84**
Mosco Greco [–]	693	**198**
sua radica	684 [verso]	**188**
N		
Napello	527	**29**
Narciso Autunnale	551.	**53**
P.^{o}	622	**125**
2.º	622	**125**
3.º	622	**125**
6.º del Matthiolo	623.	**126**
Altro	624.	**127**
Nerio	531. [530]	**32**
O		
Ombilico di Venere	559	**61**
Orecchia di lepre [–]	652.	**155**
Ortica p.^{a}	562.	**64**
2.^{a}	563.	**65**
Osiride	606.	**109**
Osteocoilon [Osteocollon]	666.	**170**
P		
Pannigella vedi herba rozza		
Papaveri	503 sino à 510.	**5–12**
cornuto	501. 502	**3–4**
domestico	500.	**2**
salvatico	499.	**1**
Paronichia vedi Capel venere		
Perfoliata	579 [574]	**76**
Personata	573.	**75**
Pianta massima	692.	**196**
Piede de sparvier [–]	664.	**168**
Piramidale	697.	**202**
Poligala	605.	**108**

[*fol. 213*]

Polipodio	640	**143**
Pomidoro	521.	**23**
Porcacchia salvatica [–] vedi semp'vivo min.^{re}		
Pseudo narciso luteo	625.	**128**
Pugnitopo [–] vedi Ruscho		
R		
Radica di China [–]	656	**160**
Rhododaphne. vedi Nerio		
Ricino	626	**129**
Rusco	610.	**113**

II. Index by 'Pozzo' number

[*fol. 214*]

Apocino	529.	**31**
Nerio o sij Rhododaphne	530	**32**
Boleti	531.	**33**
Fongo Porcino	532	**34**
Capriolini Manine	533	**35**
Prugnoli	534	**36**
Spugnolo	535	**37**
Carpanelli	536.	**38**
d'Olmo	537	**39**
Prataroli [–]	538	**40**
Bessa di lupo	539	**41**
Altri fonghi	540 à 549	**42–51**
Colchico	550	**52**
Altro, o ver Narciso Aut.^{le}	551.	**53**
Hermodattilo vero	552	**54**
Helsine	553.	**55**
Alsine	554	**56**
Semprevivo mag.^{re} e suo fiore.	555. 556	**57–58**
Vermicolare Altro Minore Minimo	557.	**59**
Montano	558	**60**
Omblico di Venere	559.	**61**
Cimbalo	560	**62**
Cimbalaria	561.	**63**
Ortica P.^{a}	562	**64**
2.^{a}	563.	**65**
Cardiaca	564	**66**
Scrofolaria	565	**67**
Gallio	566	**68**
Senecio o vero Crescione	567.	**69**
Altro	568	**70**
Verbasco, o sia Tasso barbasso	569	**71**
Fior di P.^{a} Vera	570	**72**
Maggiore	571.	**73**
Ethiopide	572	**74**
Personata ò vero Lappa	573	**75**
Perfoliata	574	**76**
Elleborina	575	**77**
Fumaria	576.	**79**
Altra	577	**80**
Coridali	578.	**81**
Loto urb.^{o} o vero tribolo	579	**82**
Sopraciglio di Venere	580.	**83**
Miride	581.	**84**
Angelica odorata	582	**85**
Altra	583	**86**
Aster Attico	584	**87**
Altro	585.	**88**

Amello di Vergilio	586	**89**
Viole mammole	587.	**90**
Iaccea, over Suocer'e Nuora [–]	588: 589	**91–92**
Buglossa o sia Borag^{e} }	590	**93**
dal fior bianco }		
dal fior turch.º	591.	**94**
volgare	592	**95**
Cinoglossa volgare	593.	**96**
Bislingue o vero hippoglosso	594	**97**

[*fol. 214v.*]

Antirrhino P.º	595	**98**
Altri	596	**99**
2.º	597.	**100**
3.º	598.	**101**
Capelvenere	599.	**102**
bianco	600.	**103**
Trichomane	601.	**104**
Xanthio	602	**105**
Egilopa	603: 604	**106–107**
Poligala	605.	**108**
Osiride	606.	**109**
Smilace aspera	607.	**110**
Vilucchio mag.^{re}	608	**111**
Luppolo	609	**112**
Rusco o sij Pugnitopo	610	**113**
Elleboro bianco	611.	**114**
Nero falso	612	**115**
Nero vero	613.	**116**
Cocomero salvatico	614	**117**
Staphisagria	615	**118**
Ginestra	616.	**119**
Spetie di Ginestra	617.	**120**
Siringa del fior turch.º	617 [618]	**121**
del fior b.º	619. 620	**122–123**
Benbianco	621.	**124**
Narciso	622.	**125**
6º	623	**126**
Bianco	624	**127**
Pseudonarciso luteo	625.	**128**
Ricino	626.	**129**
Titimalo helioscopio }	627.	**130**
characia }		
ciparissio }		
Scamonea minor di Plinio	628.	**131**
Olivella	629	**132**
Sambuco aquatico	630	**133**
Epitimo	631	**134**
Cuscuta	632.	**135**
Vite salvatica	633	**136**

Frutti di Vite nera	634	**137**
Vite bianca, o sia brionia	635.	**138**
Fiori di Vite Nera	636	**139**
Balsamini	637: 638	**140–141**
Altri	639	**142**
Polipodio	640	**143**
Driopteri	641	**144**
Cnico o sij Zaffer.^{o} saracin.^{o}	642	**145**
Mercorella femina } maschia	643	**146**
Elitropio mag.^{re} o sia scorpiuro	644	**147**
Altro	645.	**148**
Caltha	646: 647.	**149–150**
Pulianta	648	**151**
Garofani Indiani	649	**152**
minori	650	**153**
Scorpiode	651.	**154**
Orecchia di lepre [–]	652	**155**
Vite vinifera Nera	653.	**156**
vinifera b.^{a}	654	**157**
Agresto	655.	**159**
Radica di China [–]	656.	**160**
Acera mag.^{re}	657. 658	**161–162**
Sambucella o sij lauro salv.^{o}	659.	**163**
Fior di scopo	660.	**164**
Tabacco o vero herba Sta	661.	**165**
variata	662	**166**
Tertionaria	663.	**167**
Pie di Sparviero	664	**168**
Fiamma del grano	665.	**169**
Osteocoilon [Osteocollon]	666	**170**
Isapi [–]	667	**171**
Fanace	668.	**172**
Herba Maravig.^{a}	669	**173**
Coda volpina	670: 671.	**174–175**
Scopo Marino	672	**176**
Crociata	673	**177**
Cerquella	674	**178**
Sangue di Drago	675.	**179**
Coda di Sorce	676.	**180**
Radica di dente di Cane	677.	**181**
Pannigella o herba rozza	688. [678]	**182**

[*fol. 215*]

Elleborina	679	**183**
Contrierua [Contrierva]	680	**184**
Vetreca [–]	683.	**187**
Viola gialla pulianta	684	**188**
Radica di Mosco greco	684 [verso]	**188**
Viola del Perù	685	**189**

WATERMARK TYPES

Of the 293 drawings catalogued in the present volume, the watermarks of those on the pages of the *Erbario Miniato* (**1–211**) may easily be studied, whereas the remainder are mostly laid down on thick eighteenth-century mount sheets (bearing watermarks of the Dutch firm, D&C Blauw), greatly hindering the examination of their watermarks. Usually only a general description of these watermarks, from examining the sheets in raking light, has been possible; these descriptions have been given in the head-matter of the relevant catalogue entries, but the watermarks have not been typed and thus do not appear in the list below.

The watermarks in the *Erbario* itself are remarkable for their diversity. It is usual for the watermarks of a single coherent manuscript to be of only a small number of distinct types. Here, however, we find almost fifty different distinguishable types (though a number of these constitute related groups), many in single instances, lending weight to the supposition that the *Erbario* and its related volumes were compiled over a substantial period of time. However, examination of the groups of drawings that share a common watermark – such as Eagle 15 or Fleur de lys 49 – or those that share closely related types – such as Eagle 14–22 or Fleur de lys 44–57 – fails to reveal any apparent pattern of compilation. The drawings within these types, or groups of types, show no common stylistic or technical traits that they do not also appear to share with drawings on unrelated paper. Similarly, the drawings on sheets with unique watermarks – such as Flower 4 – do not seem to be different in any significant way from the rest of the material (the exception being **160**, whose uniqueness within the Erbario is discussed under that catalogue entry).

As might be expected of a volume compiled in the early years of the seventeenth century for Federico Cesi, few of the watermarks occur elsewhere in Cassiano's Paper Museum, and those occurrences appear to be coincidental rather than significant. The watermark on the index sheets (Figure 1), however, is of a type also found on a number of drawings that may be dated to the main period of Cassiano's collecting, around the 1630s, reinforcing the supposition (should it need reinforcing) that the indexes were compiled after the volume had passed into Cassiano's ownership in 1633.

Watermark	Drawing (cat. no.)
Anchor 29	**38**
Anchor 30	**51, 158**
Bird 14	**46**
Bird 19	**195**
Bird 20	**164**
Crown 5	**36, 53, 103, 186**
Crown 43	**5**
Crown 46	**76, 113**
Crown 47	**1**
Crown 48	**163**
Eagle 14	**18, 102, 104, 136**
Eagle 15	**26, 71, 88, 98, 108, 118, 122, 162, 166, 169, 175, 190, 196, 203**
Eagle 16	**90**
Eagle 17	**77, 97**
Eagle 18	**17, 23, 29, 91, 101, 116, 124, 125, 130, 137, 144, 147, 154, 168, 178**
Eagle 19	**4, 63, 100, 150**
Eagle 20	**11, 12**
Eagle 21	**74**
Eagle 22	**89, 127**
Figure 1	*Erbario Miniato,* index fols 212 and 214
Figure 15	**283**
Figure 54	**35**
Figure 56	**121**
Figure 58c	**281**
Fleur de lys 17	**159, 208**
Fleur de lys 34	**192**
Fleur de lys 44	**24, 81**
Fleur de lys 45	**188**
Fleur de lys 46	**41, 45, 60**
Fleur de lys 47	**92, 187**
Fleur de lys 48	**184, 200**
Fleur de lys 49	**21, 106, 66, 110, 138, 153**
Fleur de lys 50	**6, 8, 58, 145, 267**
Fleur de lys 51	**86, 132, 139, 173, 265**
Fleur de lys 52	**7, 176, 266**
Fleur de lys 53	**16, 276**
Fleur de lys 54	**62**
Fleur de lys 55	**199, 228, 261**
Fleur de lys 56	**47**
Fleur de lys 57	**202**
Fleur de lys 71	**181**
Flower 4	**85**
Hand 2 (cut)	**160**
Hills 9	*Erbario Miniato,* front blank fols 2–3, rear blank fols 1–2
Lamb 5	**128**
Lamb 6	**49, 126**
Lamb 7	**141**
Letter 19	**197**
Star 4	**117, 222, 236**

Anchor 29

Anchor 30

Bird 14

Bird 19

Bird 20

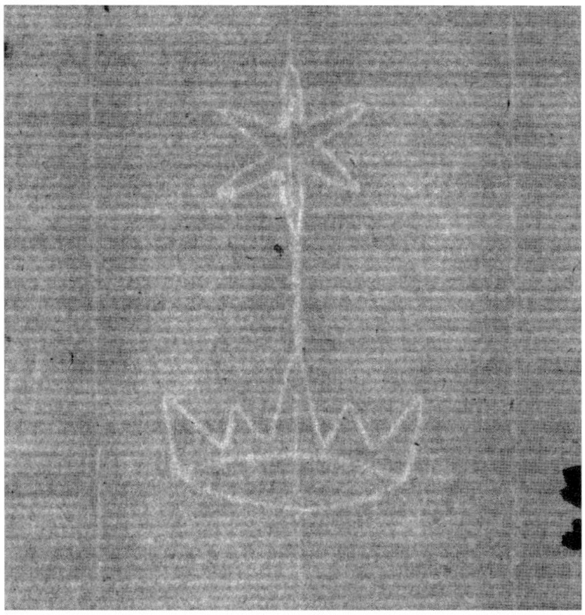

Crown 5

Crown 43

Crown 46

Crown 47

Crown 48

Eagle 14

Eagle 15

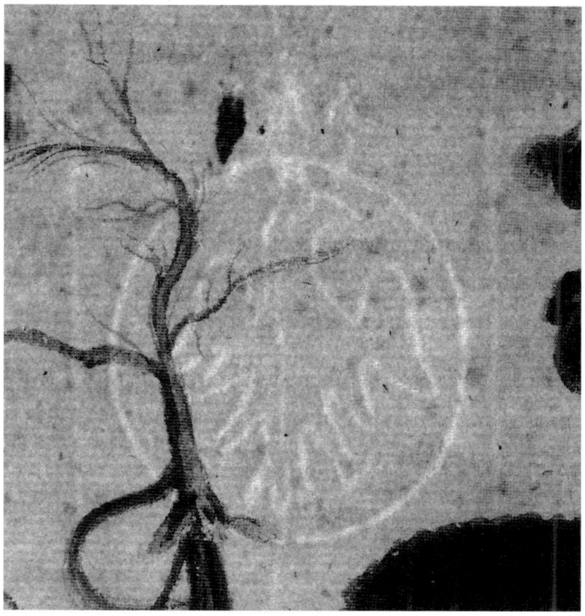

Eagle 16

Eagle 17

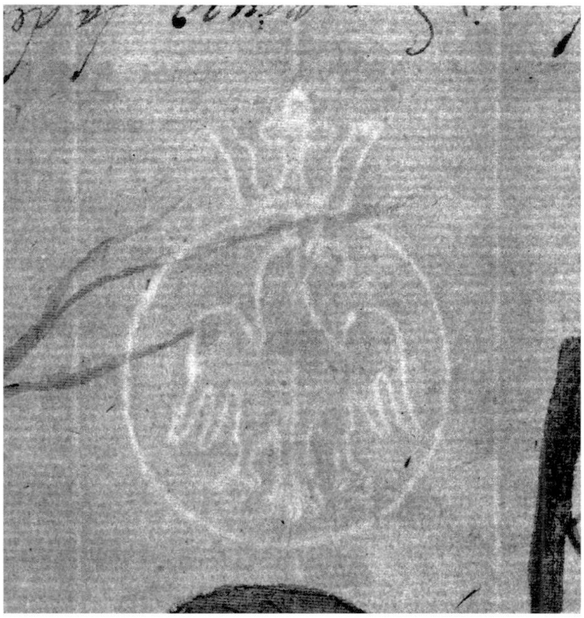

Eagle 18

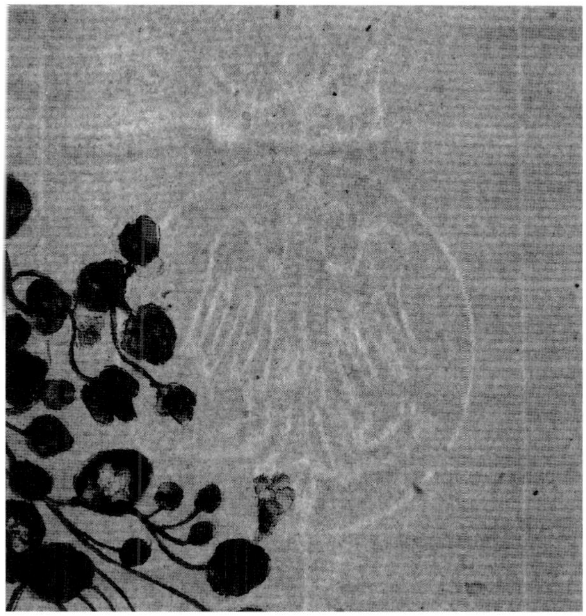

Eagle 19

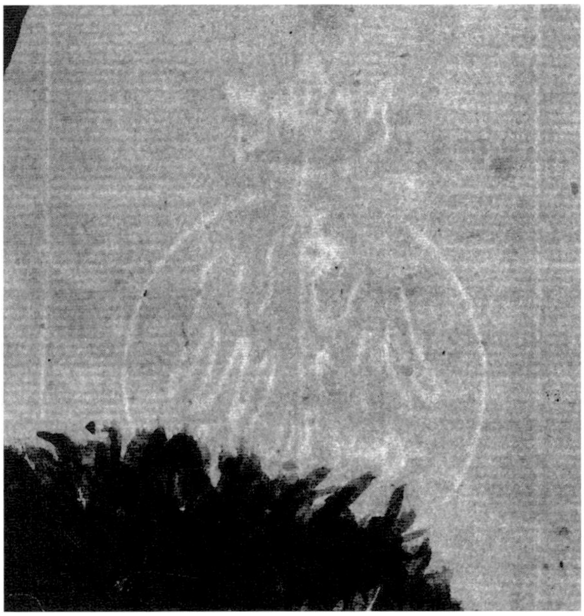
Eagle 20

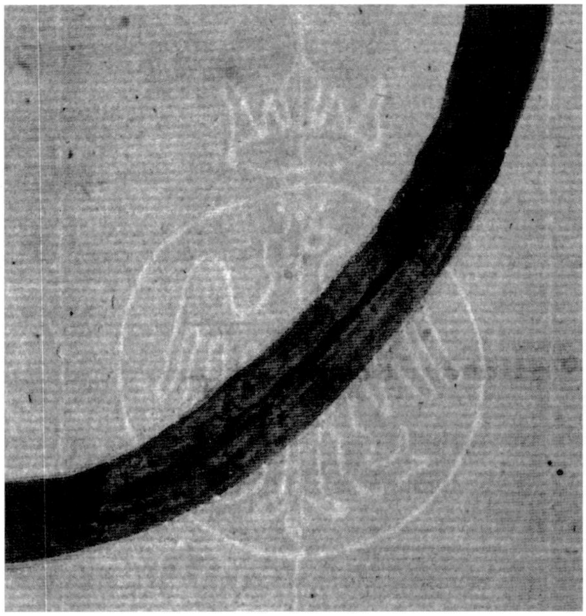
Eagle 22

Figure 1

Figure 15

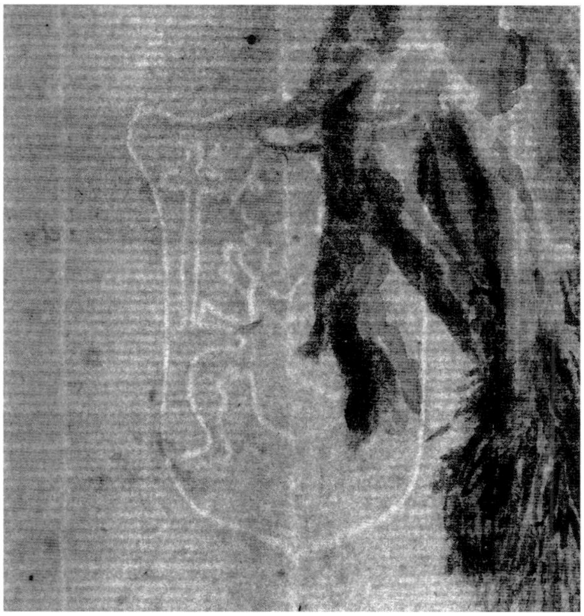
Figure 54

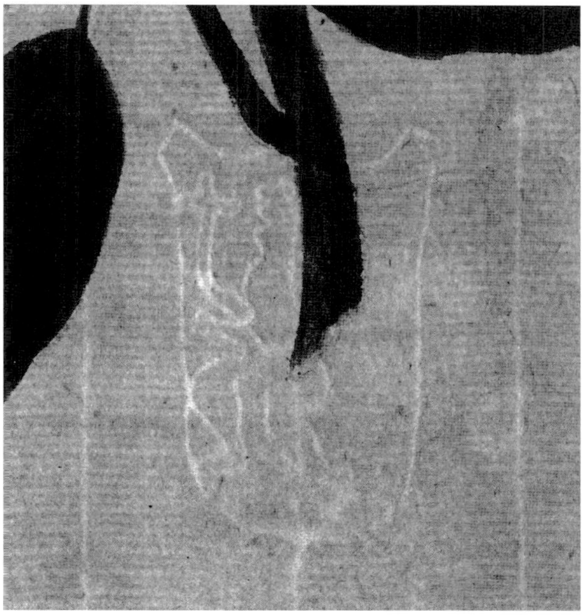
Figure 56

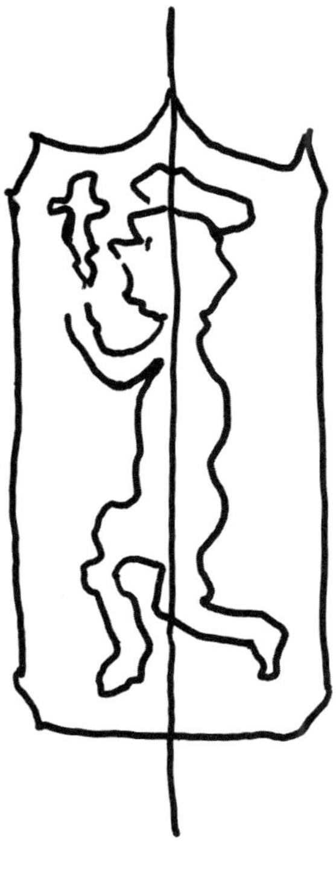
Figure 58c

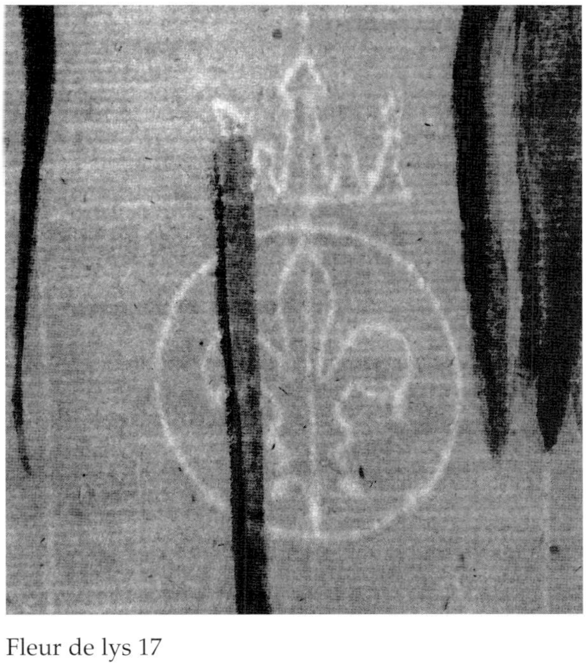
Fleur de lys 17

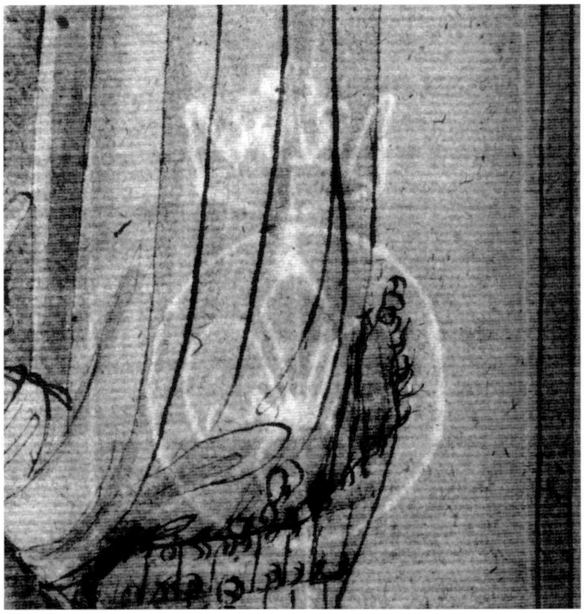

Fleur de lys 34

Fleur de lys 44

Fleur de lys 45

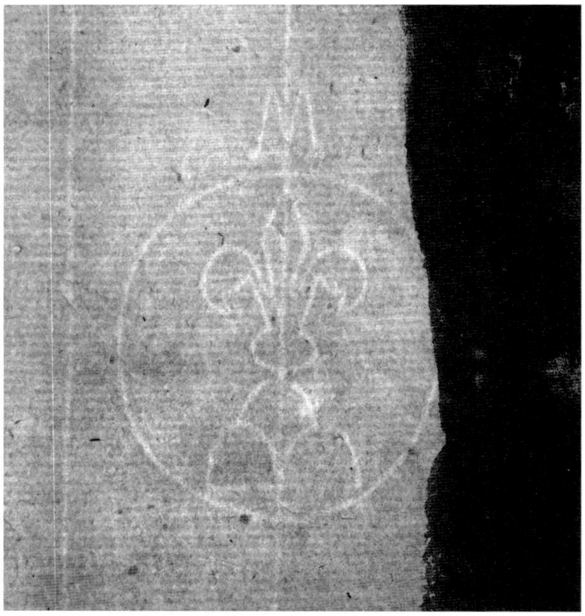

Fleur de lys 46

Fleur de lys 47

Fleur de lys 48

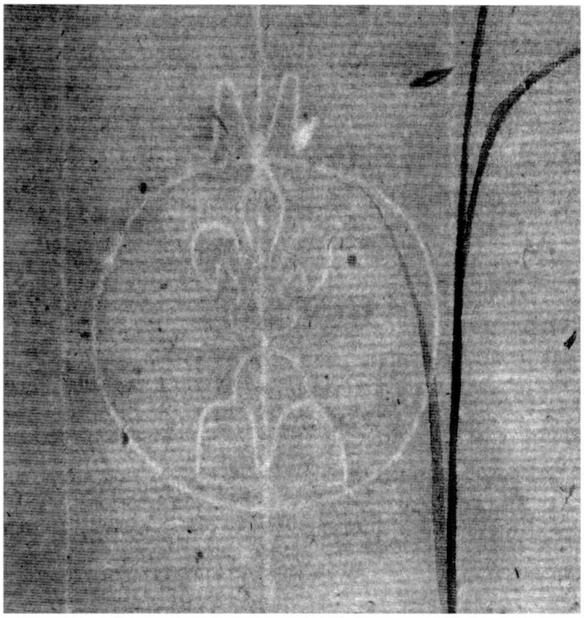

Fleur de lys 49

Fleur de lys 50

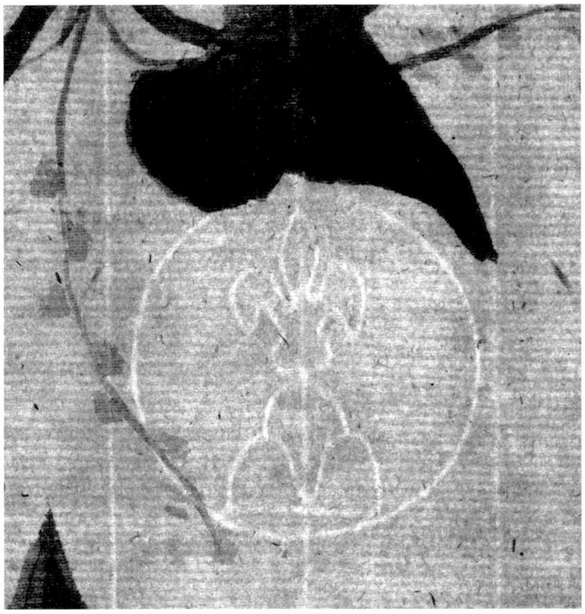

Fleur de lys 51

Fleur de lys 52

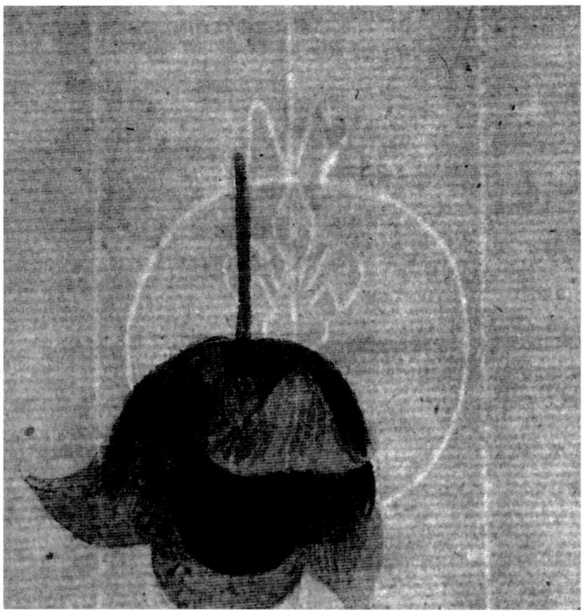

Fleur de lys 53

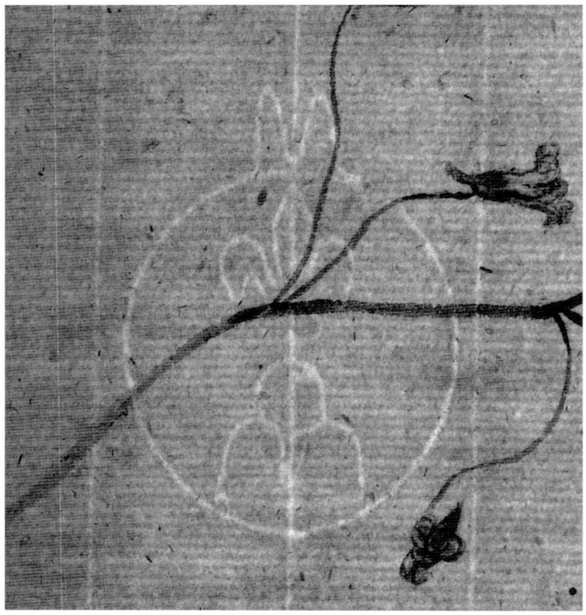

Fleur de lys 54

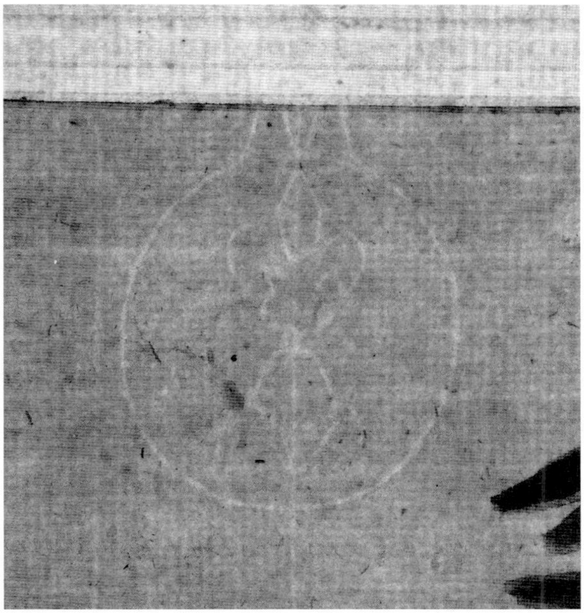

Fleur de lys 55

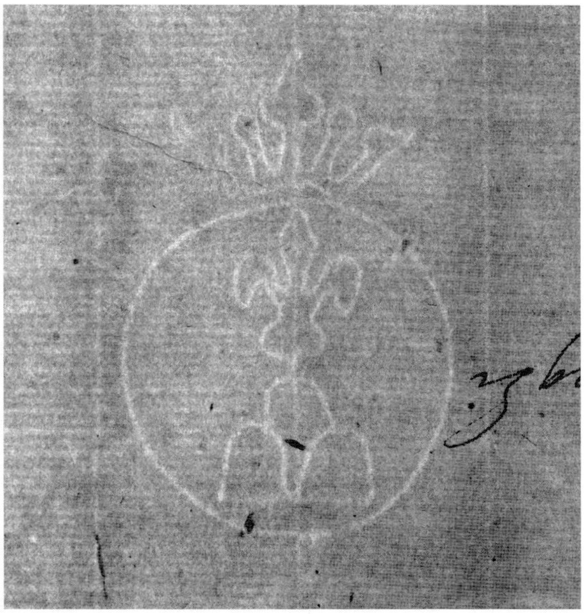

Fleur de lys 56

Fleur de lys 57

Fleur de lys 71

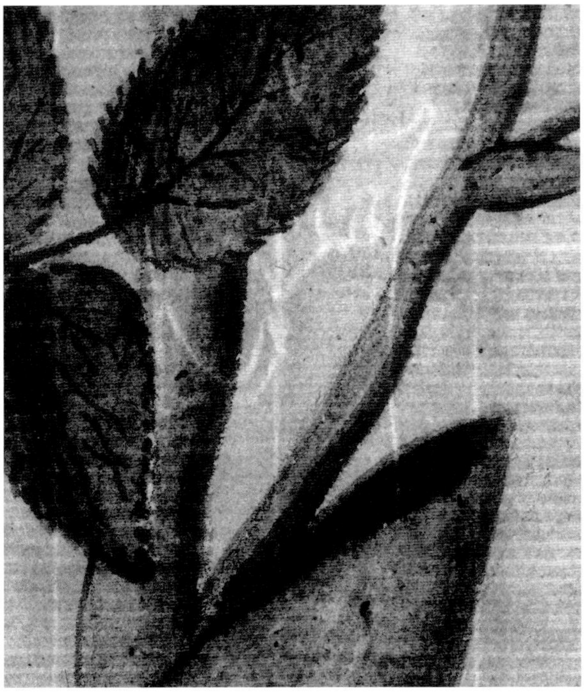

Flower 4

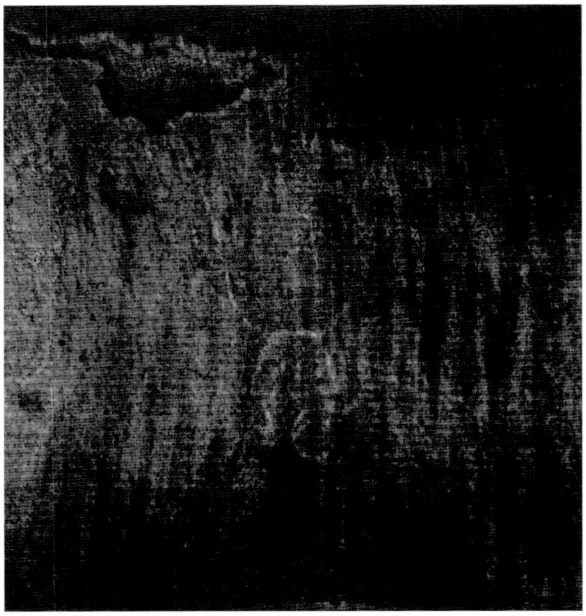

Hand 2 (cut)

Hills 9

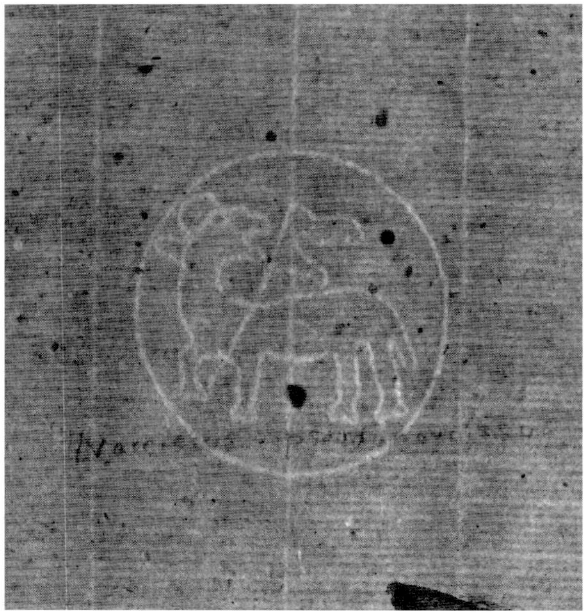

Lamb 5

Lamb 6

Lamb 7

Letter 19

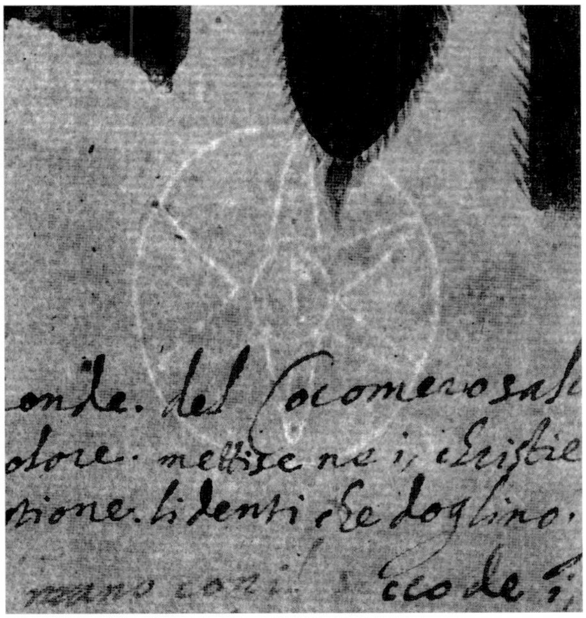

Star 4

GLOSSARY

Italic indicates that terms are defined elsewhere in the glossary

achene: a small, dry, tight-skinned *fruit*, usually consisting of a single segment, which does not open along a seam

adventitious: occurring in an unusual location: of a plant, referring to an introduced, non-native plant; of a root or other structure, meaning that it develops along the stem rather than at the expected *axil*

alkaloid: compound containing nitrogen, produced by a plant

alternate: of leaves, branches, etc.: arranged in two rows on either side of a stem or axis, with the individual leaves or branches alternating rather than occurring in pairs (cf. *opposite*)

amplexicaul: referring to a leaf base that is enlarged and clasps the stem

androecium: the male organs of the plant (*anther* and *stamen*) together

annual: a plant that completes its life-cycle in a single year

anthela: a *panicle* whose side axes exceed the main axis in length

anther: the pollen-bearing portion of the *stamen*

anthesis: flowering: the opening of the flower, the period in which the plant is fertile

apex: growing tip

astringent: (a substance) causing body tissues to contract

awn: a sharp point or bristle on a *bract* of a grass

axil: the angle between an axis and a structure that branches off from it

basal: arising from the base or point of attachment of a plant or organ

biennial: a plant with a two-year life-cycle, generally flowering in the second year

bilabial: with two lips

bipartite: composed of two parts

blade: the expanded part of a leaf or *petal*

bract: a modified leaf that *subtends* the *inflorescence*, protecting the stem and flowers

bracteate: bearing *bracts*

caespitose: growing in small, thick clumps or mats

calcareous: of soil: chalky or alkaline

calyx: the outer layer of the *perianth*; the ring of *sepals* that surrounds the *petals* and sexual organs

capitulum: a densely clustered head of usually *sessile* flowers on an axis

capsule: a *fruit* which splits open along a defined seam to release the *seeds*

carina: a keel-shaped structure

carpel: a single *pistil*, or one component of a compound pistil

cladode: a photosynthetic branch; a portion of stem that acts like a leaf

cladophyll: a stem simulating a leaf

collar: the swollen base of a branch or stem

cordate: heart-shaped, with the indentation at the base (cf. *obcordate*)

corm: a swollen underground stem, or base of a stem, that is produced annually

corolla: the inner *whorl* of the *perianth*; the ring of *petals* surrounded by the *calyx*

corymb: an *inflorescence*, usually flat-topped, in which the outer flowers open first (cf. *cyme*)

cultivar: a cultivated variety; a plant that is either raised in cultivation or owes its distinct identity to being maintained in cultivation

cyme: an *inflorescence*, usually flat-topped, in which the central or terminal flower opens first (cf. *corymb*)

depurative: purifying or removing toxins from the body

dioecious: with male and female flowers on separate plants

distal: furthest from the axis

diuretic: provoking urination

doctrine of signatures: the notion that a natural remedy (usually a plant) will indicate by its appearance the part of the body it heals: so walnuts, with their convoluted surfaces, are deemed to have healing properties for the brain

emetic: provoking vomiting

emollient: soothing, especially of the skin

epicalyx: a false *calyx*; an *involucre* of *bracts* surrounding a calyx

excentric: one-sided, away from the centre

expectorant: provoking coughing

filiform: long and slender

fimbriate: finely fringed

fruit: the ripened *ovary* of a plant, the structure containing the fertilized *seeds*

fruit-body: the spore-bearing organ of mushrooms

galea: a helmet-shaped structure
glabrous: smooth, hairless
glomerule: a group of *capitula* or clusters of flowers, *subtended* by a single *involucre*
gynoecium: the female portion of a flower; the *pistil* or pistils
gynomonoecious: with separate female and *hermaphrodite* flowers on the same plant

haemostatic: suppressing bleeding
heliotropic: turning in the direction of the sun
herbaceous: lacking woody parts or permanent upright stems
hermaphrodite: with both male and female parts in the same flower; see *monoclinous*

inflorescence: a cluster of flowers, all arising from the main stem or *peduncle*
involucre: a *bract*, or *whorl* of small bracts, *subtending* a flower or *inflorescence*

labellum: lip
laciniate: divided into narrow pointed *lobes*
lanceolate: lance- or spear-shaped
lax: loose rather than dense
lemma: in grasses, the lower and thicker of two *bracts* which enclose the flower
liana: a woody vine
ligulate: strap-shaped, or with a strap-shaped appendage
lobe: a segment separated from the rest of the structure by an indentation

margin: edge
mericarp: a portion of an *ovary* which splits apart at maturity, each portion containing a single *seed*
monoclinous: with male and female organs in the same flower (used only of angiosperms, or flowering plants)
monoecious: with separate male and female flowers on the same plant
mucilage: a viscous liquid or gluey substance
mucronate: terminating with a spine (mucro) arising from the midrib
mutagenic: mutation-inducing

naturalized: of a non-native, introduced plant: established in the wild, and reproducing without human assistance
nerve: rib or vein
node: the point on an axis where one or more structures (leaves, flowers) are attached

obcordate: heart-shaped, but with the indentation at the *apex* (cf. *cordate*)
obovate: *ovate*, but broadest above rather than below the middle
opposite: referring to two organs at the same level, or at *nodes*, but on opposite sides of the axis (cf. *alternate*)
ovary: the *basal* part of a *pistil*; the portion of the flower in which the *seed* develops
ovate: egg-shaped; rounded at both ends but broadest below the middle (cf. *obovate*)

palmate: with three or more *lobes*, veins or other structures which originate and spread outwards from the same point
panicle: a branched *inflorescence*, in which the lower flowers open first
papilionaceous: butterfly-shaped
pappus: a *whorl* of delicate bristles in place of the *calyx*
partite: divided almost to the base
pedicel: a small stalk that supports an individual flower within an *inflorescence*
peduncle: a stalk that supports an entire *inflorescence*
perfoliate: referring to a *sessile* leaf whose *basal lobes* are united, so that the stem seems to pass through the *blade*
perianth: the *calyx* and *corolla* together; the group of floral envelopes
perennial: a plant whose life-cycle lasts three seasons or more
petal: one of the modified leaves of the *corolla*, the inner *whorl* of the *perianth*
petiole: leaf stalk
pinna: a feather-life arrangement, or one of a series of leaflets arranged in two rows along the *rachis*
pistil: the female reproductive structure of a flower; the *ovary*, *style* (or *stylus*) and *stigma* together
poricidal: of an *anther*: where pollen is released through pores at the *apex*
proximate: the nearest portion
pseudolateral: where the *basal involucral bract* appears to be a continuation of the stem
purgative: provoking defecation
pyx (or **pyxis**): a *capsule* which opens like a lid to release the *seed*

quiescent: dormant

raceme: an unbranched *inflorescence* composed of flowers with individual *pedicels* or stalks, whose lower flowers open first
rachis: the axis or central stem of a compound leaf or *inflorescence*

reflexed: bent down or out at an angle greater than 90 degrees
rhizome: a specialized stem, either underground or lying close to the surface, that produces stems or leaves at intervals along its length
rosette: a group of leaves radiating from a common crown or centre

samara: a single-seeded winged *fruit* that splits open along a seam
scape: an erect leafless stalk that develops near the ground and carries a flower or *inflorescence*
scapose: carrying a flower or *inflorescence* on a *scape*
seed: a plant embryo: a ripened, fertilized ovule
senescence: the process that follows maturity and leads to the death of tissue
sepal: one of the modified leaves of the *calyx*, the outer *whorl* of the *perianth*
septum: a wall or partition
sessile: stalkless, or with a minimal stalk (subsessile)
siliqua: a thin *fruit* with two *carpels*, that splits open longitudinally along a seam and leaves a *septum* or partition behind
sorus: in ferns: a cluster of *sporangia*, found on the underside of the leaf *blade*
spathe: a large leaf or *bract subtending* and partially enclosing a fleshy *inflorescence* or spadix
spatulate: shaped like a spatula: oblong, but rounded at the *apex*
specific: a substance which has an effect on a particular disease or injury
spike, spikelet: an *inflorescence* with *sessile* flowers on an unbranched axis, and in which the lower flowers open first
spinule: small spine
sporangium: a spore-containing or spore-producing structure
sport: a plant that shows some significant variation on the normal morphology (colour or shape of leaves, doubling of flower, etc.), which can result in a new *cultivar* if propagated vegetatively, but whose distinctive feature is not transmitted through sexual reproduction
spur: a tubular extension of the *perianth*
stamen: the male sexual organ in a flower, bearing an *anther* which produces pollen
stigma: the tip of the *style*, usually differing in shape or texture from the rest of the style; the portion of the female sexual organ which receives the pollen
stigmatic: attached to the *stigma*: the pollen-receiving tip of the female organ in the flower
stipule: an appendage, resembling a leaf or *bract*, at the base of a *petiole* or leaf stalk
stolon: a prostrate stem or runner, which can take root and give rise to new plants or plantlets
stoma: a pore in a leaf surface, usually on the underside, through which gases enter and leave the leaf
style, stylus: the long, thin part of the *pistil*, terminating in the *stigma*
subtend: to be inserted directly below another organ or structure, often sheathing or enclosing it
sudorific: provoking sweating

taproot: the primary root, which anchors the plant in addition to obtaining nutrition
tepal: a modified leaf of an undifferentiated *perianth*, whose parts are not distinguishable as *sepal* or *petal*
tomentose: with a dense clump of woolly, rigid hairs
tuber: a swollen root, stem or branch, used for food storage, and generally underground
tubercle: a small, warty outgrowth
tunic: a loose, dry, papery skin covering a bulb or *corm*

umbel: a flat-topped *inflorescence*, in which all the *pedicels* arise from a common point at the *apex* of the stem or branch

verticil: a *whorl* with three or more parts arising from a single *node*
verticillaster: a false *whorl*: where *opposite cymes* appear to surround the stem in a whorl
verticillate: forming a *whorl*

whorl: a circular arrangement of three or more organs arising from the same *node*; used generally of flowers, though it can apply to other organs as well

BIBLIOGRAPHY OF SPECIES AUTHORITIES

Andersson	N.J. Andersson, 'Om de med *Saccharum* beslägtade genera', *Öfversigt af Kungl. Vetenskaps-Akademiens Förhandlingar*, XII, 1855, pp. 151–68
L.H. Bailey	L.H. Bailey, *Manual of Cultivated Plants*, rev. edn, New York 1949
Bernh.	J.J. Bernhardi, *Systematische Verzeichnis der Pflanzen, welche in der Gegend um Erfurt gefunden werden*, Erfurt 1800
Bertol.	A. Bertoloni, *Flora Italica sistens plantas in Italia et in insulis circumstantibus sponte nascentes*, 10 vols, Bologna 1833–54
Borkh.	M.B. Borkhausen, in J.J. Roemer, *Archiv für die Botanik*, I/2, p. 45, Leipzig 1797
Brummitt	R.K. Brummitt, 'Further new names in the genus *Calystegia* (Convolvulaceae)', *Kew Bulletin*, XXXV, 1980, pp. 327–34
Bull.	P. Bulliard, *Herbier de la France ou collection complète des plantes indigènes de ce royaume; avec leurs détails anatomiques, leurs propriétés, et leurs usages en médecine*, Paris 1780–93
Cassini	A.H.G. de Cassini, 'Pallénide', in *Dictionnaire des sciences naturelles*, XXXVII, pp. 275–6, Paris 1825
Cassini ex Spach	A.H.G. de Cassini, in E. Spach, *Histoire naturelle des végétaux: Phanérogames*, X, p. 181, Paris 1841
Crantz	H.J.N. von Crantz, *Stirpium Austriacarum*, 2 vols, Vienna 1762–7
Dandy	J.E. Dandy, in H.J. Riddelsdell *et al.*, *Flora of Gloucestershire*, p. 611, Cheltenham 1948
DC	A.P. de Candolle, 'Sur les champignons parasites', *Annales du Muséum d'Histoire Naturelle*, IX, 1807, p. 56
Desf.	R.L. Desfontaines, 'Balsamita', *Actes de la Société d'Histoire Naturelle de Paris*, I, 1792, pp. 1–3
Druce	G.C. Druce, 'On the nomenclature of British plants as affected by the law adopted by the botanical congress at Vienna', *Annals of Scottish Natural History*, no. 60, 1906, pp. 217–29
Duchesne	A.N. Duchesne, in J.B.A.P. de Monnet de Lamarck, *Encylopédie méthodique: botanique*, II, p. 151, Paris 1786
Ehrh. ex Hoffm.	J.F. Ehrhart, in G.F. Hoffmann, *Deutschlands Flora*, 2nd edn, II, p. 18, Erlangen 1795
Fr.	E.M. Fries, *Systema mycologicum, sistens fungorum ordines, genera et species, huc usque cognitas, quas ad normam methodi naturalis determinavit, disposuit atque descripsit*, 3 vols, Greifswald 1821–32
P. Gaertn.	P.G. Gaertner, B. Meyer and J. Scherbius, *Oekonomisch-technische Flora der Wetterau*, II, p. 397, Frankfurt am Main 1800
Garbari	F. Garbari, 'Il genere *Muscari* Miller in Italia', *Giornale Botanico Italiano*, CIII, 1970, p. 613
Garcke	C.A.F. Garcke, *Flora von Nord- und Mittel-Deutschland*, 9th edn, Berlin 1864
Gay	J. Gay, in C.R.A. des Moulins, *Catalogue raisonné des plantes qui croissent spontanément dans le département de la Dordogne*, p. 12, Bordeaux 1840
S.F. Gray	S.F. Gray, *A Natural Arrangement of British Plants, according to their relation to each other*, London 1821
Griseb.	A.H.R. Grisebach, *Spicilegium florae Rumelicae et Bithynicae*, 2 vols, Braunschweig 1843–5
Hill	J. Hill, *The Vegetable System*, London 1759–75
Huds.	W. Hudson, *Flora Anglica, exhibens plantas per regnum Angliae sponte crescentes, distributas secundum systema sexuale: cum differentiis specierum, synonymis auctorum, nominibus incolarum, solo locorum, tempore florendi, officinalibus pharmacopaeorum*, London 1762
Jaap	O. Jaap, 'Achtes Verzeichnis zu meinem Exsiccatenwerk "*Fungi selecti exsiccati*"', *Verhandlungen des Botanischen Vereins der Provinz Brandenburg, Berlin*, 59, 1917, pp. 24–40

Jacq. 1764	N.J. Jacquin, *Observationum botanicarum iconibus ab auctore delineatis illustratarum*, I, p. 32, Vienna 1764
Jacq. 1774	N.J. Jacquin, *Florae Austriacae, sive plantarum selectarum in Austriae Archiducatu sponte crescentium, icones, ad vivum coloratae, et descriptionibus, ac synonymis illustratae*, II, p. 59, Vienna 1774
A. Juss.	A.H.L. de Jussieu, *De Euphorbiacearum generibus medicisque earundem viribus tentamen*, Paris 1824
Ker Gawl. ex Sprengel	J.B. Ker Gawler, in C.P.J. Sprengel, *Caroli Linnaei ... systema vegetabilium*, 16th edn, II, p. 57, Göttingen 1825
A. Kern.	A. Kerner von Marilaun, *Monographia Pulmonariarum*, Innsbruck 1878
W.D.J. Koch	W.D.J. Koch, *Synopsis florae Germanicae et Helveticae, exhibens stirpes phanerogamas rite cognitas, quae in Germania, Helvetia, Borussia et Istria sponte crescunt atque in hominum usum copiosius coluntur, secundum systema Candolleanum digestas, praemissa generum dispositione, secundum classes et ordines systematis Linnaeani conscripta*, Frankfurt am Main 1835–7
Korf	R.P. Korf, 'Some new discomycete names', *Phytologia*, XXI/4, 1971, pp. 201–7
Kumm.	P. Kummer, *Der Führer in die Pilzkunde: Anleitung zum methodischen, leichten und sichern Bestimmen der in Deutschland vorkommenden Pilze*, Zerbst 1871
Kuntze	O. Kuntze, *Revisio generum plantarum*, II, p. 541, Leipzig 1891
L.	C. von Linné [Linnaeus], *Species plantarum, exhibentes plantas rite cognitas, ad genera relatas, cum differentiis specificis, nominibus trivialibus, synonymis selectis, locis natalibus, secundum systema sexuale digestas*, Stockholm 1753
L. 1754	C. Linnaeus, *Genera plantarum eorumque characteres naturales secundum numerum, figuram, situm, et proportionem omnium fructificationis partium*, Stockholm 1754
L. 1758–9	C. Linnaeus, *Systema naturae*, 10th edn, 1758–9
L. 1762–3	C. Linnaeus, *Species plantarum*, 2nd edn, 2 vols, Stockholm 1762–3
L. 1771	C. Linnaeus, *Mantissa plantarum altera*, Stockholm 1771
Lam. 1778	J.B.A.P. de Monnet de Lamarck, *Flore françoise ou description succincte de toutes les plantes qui croissent naturellement en France, disposée selon une nouvelle méthode d'analyse*, 3 vols, Paris 1778
Lam. 1801	J.B.A.P. de Monnet de Lamarck, *Système des animaux sans vertèbres, ou tableau général des classes, des ordres et des genres de ces animaux*, Paris 1801
Lapeyr.	P.P. de Lapeyrouse, *Histoire abrégée des plantes des Pyrénées*, Toulouse 1813
Link	J.H.F. Link, *Enumeratio plantarum horti regii botanici Berolinensis altera*, 2 vols, Berlin 1821–2
Loisel.	J.L.A. Loiseleur-Deslongchamps, *Nouvelle notice sur les plantes à ajouter à la flore de France*, Paris 1810
Mack. & Bush	K.K. Mackenzie and B.F. Bush, 'New plants from Missouri', *16th Annual Report of the Missouri Botanical Garden*, 1905, pp. 102–8
V.A. Matthews	V.A. Matthews, 'Senecio', in B. Davis (ed.), *Flora of Turkey and the East Aegean Islands*, V, 1975, pp. 145–68
Medik. 1787	F.K. Medikus, 'Versuch einer neuen Lehrart die Pflanzen nach zwei Methoden angleich, nehmlich nach der künstlichen und natürlichen, zu ordnen', *Vorlesungen der Churpfälzichen physikalisch-ökonomischen Gesellschaft*, II, 1787, pp. 327–461
Medik. 1790	F.K. Medikus, 'Ueber den gynandrischen Situs der Staubfäden und Pistille einiger Pflanzen', in *Historia et commentationes Academiae Electoralis Scientiarum et Elegantiorum Litterarum Theodoro-Palatinae: Physicum*, VI, pp. 374–414, Mannheim 1790
Medik. 1791	F.K. Medikus, 'Ueber Linnes Hyacinthen Gattung', in P. Usteri (ed.), *Annalen der Botanik*, II, 1791, pp. 5–20
Merr.	E.D. Merrill, *An Interpretation of Rumphius's Herbarium Amboinense*, Manila 1917
Mertens & Koch	F.K. Mertens and W.D.J. Koch, *Deutschlands Flora*, 3rd edn, 5 vols, Frankfurt am Main 1823–39
Mich.	P.A. Micheli, *Nova plantarum genera juxta Tournefortii methodum disposita*, Florence 1729

Mill.	P. Miller, *The Gardener's Dictionary*, 8th edn, 2 vols, London 1768
Moench	C. Moench, *Methodus plantas horti botanici et agri Marburgensis*, Marburg 1794
Müll	O.F. Müller, in *Flora Danica*, v, p. 14, pl. 834, Copenhagen 1870
Nyman	C.F. Nyman, *Conspectus florae Europeae*, Ãrebro 1878–90
Opiz	P.M. Opiz, *Seznam rostlin květeny České*, Prague 1852
Pallas	P.S. Pallas, *Reise durch verschiedene Provinzen des Russischen Reichs*, III, p. 537, St Petersburg 1776
Pers. 1801	C.H. Persoon, *Synopsis methodica fungorum, sistens enumerationem omnium hucusque detectarum specierum, cum brevibus descriptionibus nec non synonymis et observationibus selectis*, Göttingen 1801
Pers. 1805	C.H. Persoon, *Synopsis plantarum, seu enchiridion botanicum, complectens enumerationem systematicam specierum hucusque cognitarum*, I, p. 85, Paris 1805
Plenck	J.J. von Plenck, *Icones plantarum medicinalium*, 8 vols, Vienna 1788–1812
R. Br.	R. Brown, in W.T. Aiton, *Hortus Kewensis*, 2nd edn, IV, p. 119, London 1812
Rafn	C.G. Rafn, *Danmarks og Holsteens flora*, 2 vols, Copenhagen 1796–1800
Rchb.	H.G.L. Reichenbach, *Uebersicht der Gattung Aconitum*, Regensburg 1819
Req. ex Bertol.	E. Requien, in A. Bertoloni, *Flora Italica sistens plantas in Italia et in insulis circumstantibus sponte nascentes*, I, p. 787, Bologna 1833–4
A. Rich. 1823	A. Richard, 'Cedrus', in J.B.G.M. Bory de Saint-Vincent, *Dictionnaire classique d'histoire naturelle*, III, pp. 298–300, Paris 1823
A. Rich. 1824	A. Richard, 'Ecballium', in J.B.G.M. Bory de Saint-Vincent, *Dictionnaire classique d'histoire naturelle*, VI, pp. 19–20, Paris 1824
Ricken	A. Ricken, *Die Blätterpilze (Agaricaceae) Deutschlands und der angrenzenden Länder, besonders Oesterreichs und der Schweiz*, Leipzig 1915
Salisb. 1796	R.A. Salisbury, *Prodromus stirpium in horto ad Chapel Allerton vigentium*, London 1796
Salisb. 1807	R.A. Salisbury, 'Observations on the genera of Trollius, Eranthis, Helleborus, Coptis and Isopyrum', *Trans Linnean Soc*, VIII, 1807, pp. 300–7
Schaeffer	J.C. Schaeffer, *Fungorum qui in Bavaria et Palatinatu circa Ratisbonam nascuntur icones nativis coloribus expressae*, 4 vols, Regensburg 1762–74
K.F. Schimp.	K.F. Schimper, 'Symphytum bulbosum, eine neue Pflanzenspecies', *Flora*, VIII, 1825, pp. 17–24
Schrödinger	R. Schrödinger, 'Der Blütenbau der zygomorphen Ranunculaceen und seine Bedeutung für die Stammesgeschichte des Helleboreen', *Abhandlungen des K.K. Zoologisches-Botanisches Gesellschaft in Wien*, IV/5, 1909, pp. 1–69
Schur	P. J. F. Schur, 'Beiträge zur Kenntnis der Flora von Siebenbürgen', *Verhandlungen und Mitteilungen des siebenbürgischen Vereins für Naturwissenschaften zu Hermannstadt*, IV, 1853, pp. 46–52
Schweigg. & Kört.	A.F. Schweigger and F. Körte, *Flora Erlangensis continens plantas phaenogamas circa Erlangam crescentes*, 2 vols, Erlangen 1811
Scop.	J.A. Scopoli, *Flora Carniolica exhibens plantas Carnioliae indigenas et distributas in classes naturales cum differentiis specificis, recentiorum, locis natalibus, nominibus incolarum, observationibus selectis, viribus medicis*, 2nd rev. edn, Vienna 1772
Sibth. & Sm.	J. Sibthorp and J.E. Smith, *Florae Graecae prodromus*, 2 vols, London 1806–13
Singer 1951	R. Singer, 'The Agaricales (mushrooms) in modern taxonomy', *Lilloa*, XXII, 1951, p. 168
Singer 1962	R. Singer, in M.A. Donk, 'The generic names proposed for Agaricaceae', *Beihefte zur Nova Hedwigia*, v, 1962, pp. 1–320
Sweet	R. Sweet, *The British Flower Garden: containing coloured figures and descriptions of the most ornamental and curious hardy herbaceous plants*, 7 vols, London 1823–37
Tausch	I.F. Tausch, 'Botanische Beobachtungen', *Flora*, XII, 1829, pp. 641–50

Ten.	M. Tenore, *Flora Napolitana*, 5 vols, Naples 1811–38
Tul.	E.L.R. and C. Tulasne, 'New notes upon the Tremellineous fungi and their analogues', *J Linnean Soc (Botany)*, XIII, 1871, pp. 31–42
Vahl	M. Vahl (ed.), *Icones plantarum sponte nascentium in regnis Daniae et Norvegiae, in ducatibus Slesvici et Holsatiae, et in comitatibus Oldenburgi et Delmenhorstiae; ad illustrandum opus de iisdem plantis, regio jussu exarandum Florae Danicae nomine inscriptum; editae ab ejus operis auctore, Georgio Christiano Oeder*, VI and VIII, Copenhagen 1787–99
Vill.	D. Villars, *Histoire des plantes de Dauphiné*, 4 vols, Grenoble 1786–9
Waldst. & Kit. 1806–12	F. de P.A. von Waldstein and P. Kitaibel, *Descriptiones et icones plantarum rariorum Hungariae*, III, p. 290, Vienna 1806–12
Waldst. & Kit. 1809	F. de P.A. von Waldstein and P. Kitaibel, in C.J. Willdenow, *Enumeratio plantarum Horti Regii Botanici Berolinensis*, p. 592, Berlin 1809
Wettst. 1891	R. von Wettstein, 'Scrophulariaceae', in H.G.A. Engler and K.A.E. Prantl (eds), *Die natürlichen Pflanzenfamilien*, IV, pt 3(b), pp. 39–107, Leipzig 1891
Wettst. 1897	R. von Wettstein, in N.T. Patouillard, 'Fungi', *Catalogue Raisonné des Plantes Cellulaires de la Tunisie*, pp. 19–136, Paris 1897
Wohlf.	R. Wohlfahrt, in W.D.J. Koch, *Synopsis der Deutschen und Schweizer Flora*, 3rd edn, II, p. 714, Leipzig 1892

ABBREVIATIONS AND GENERAL BIBLIOGRAPHY

Institutions

BAV	Vatican, Biblioteca Apostolica Vaticana
Bologna, BU	Bologna, Biblioteca Universitaria
London, BL	London, British Library
Montpellier, BEM	Montpellier, Bibliothèque de l'École de Médecine
Paris, BIF	Paris, Bibliothèque de l'Institut de France
Pisa, BU	Pisa, Biblioteca Universitaria
Rome, BA	Rome, Biblioteca Angelica
Rome, BANL	Rome, Biblioteca dell'Accademia Nazionale dei Lincei
Windsor, RL	Windsor, Royal Library

Books and articles

Abbe 1965 — E. Abbe, *The Plants of Virgil's Georgics*, Ithaca, NY, 1965

Alessandrini 1976 — A. Alessandrini, 'Giovanni Heckius Linceo e la sua controversia contro i protestanti', *Rivista di Storia della Chiesa*, xxx, 1976, pp. 363–404

Alessandrini 1978 — A. Alessandrini, *Cimeli Lincei a Montpellier* (Indici e sussidi bibliografici della Biblioteca, Accademia Nazionale dei Lincei 11), Rome 1978

Alessandrini/de Angelis/Lanzara 1985 — A. Alessandrini, G. de Angelis and P. Lanzara, 'Il "Theatrum . . . Plantarum" di Federico Cesi della Biblioteca dell'Institut de France', *Atti dell'Accademia Nazionale dei Lincei. Rendiconti della classe di scienze fisiche, matematiche e naturali*, ser. VIII, LXXVIII, 1985, pp. 315–25

Amazing Rare Things 2007 — D. Attenborough, S. Owens, M. Clayton and R. Alexandratos, *Amazing Rare Things: The Art of Natural History in the Age of Discovery*, London 2007

Arber 1986 — A. Arber, *Herbals: Their Origin and Evolution*, 3rd edn, with an introduction and annotations by W.T. Stearn, Cambridge 1986

Baglione 1642 — G. Baglione, *Le vite dei pittori, scultori et architetti dal pontificato di Gregorio XIII del 1572 in fino a tempi di Papa Urbano Ottavo nel 1642*, Rome 1642

Baldriga 2002 — I. Baldriga, *L'occhio della lince. I primi Lincei tra arte, scienza e collezionismo*, Rome 2002

Besler 1613 — B. Besler, *Hortus Eystettensis, sive diligens et accurate omnium plantarum, florum, stirpium, et variis orbis terrae partibus, singulari studio collectarum . . .*, Eichstatt 1613

Blunt/Raphael 1979 — W. Blunt and S. Raphael, *The Illustrated Herbal*, London 1979

Blunt/Raphael 1989 — W. Blunt and S. Raphael, *Gli erbari*, Turin 1989 (Italian edn of Blunt/Raphael 1979)

Brevaglieri *et al.* 2007 — S. Brevaglieri, L. Guerrini, F. Solinas, *Sul Tesoro Messicano e su alcuni disegni del Museo Cartaceo di Cassiano dal Pozzo*, Rome 2007

Carutti 1883 — D. Carutti, *Breve storia dell'Accademia dei Lincei*, Rome 1883

Cassiano cat. 1993 — *The Paper Museum of Cassiano dal Pozzo* (*Quaderni Puteani* 4), exhib. cat., London and Milan 1993

Cassiano cat. 1997 — *Cassiano dal Pozzo's Paper Museum: Drawings from the Royal Collection*, H. McBurney (ed.), exhib. cat., Edinburgh 1997

Cassiano Segreti 2000 — *I segreti di un collezionista. Le straordinarie raccolte di Cassiano dal Pozzo 1588–1657*, F. Solinas (ed.), exhib. cat., Rome 2000

Cassiano Segreti 2001 — *I segreti di un collezionista. Le straordinarie raccolte di Cassiano dal Pozzo 1588–1657*, F. Solinas (ed.), exhib. cat., Rome 2001

Cattabiani 1996	A. Cattabiani, *Florario. Miti, leggende e simboli di fiori e piante*, Milan 1996
Cesi, *Atti* 1986	*Convegno celebrativo del IV centenario della nascita di Federico Cesi* (*Atti dei Convegni Lincei 78*), *Acquasparta, 7–9 ottobre, 1985*, Rome 1986
Cesi, *Atti* 2006	A. Graniti (ed.), *Federico Cesi: un principe naturalista* (*Atti dei Convegni Lincei 225*), *Acquasparta, 29–30 settembre 2003*, Rome 2006
Clusius 1601	C. Clusius, *Rariorum plantarum historia*, Antwerp 1601
Clusius 1605	C. Clusius, *Exoticorum libri decem: quibus animalium, plantarum, aromatum, aliorumque peregrinorum fructuum historiae describuntur . . .* , Leiden 1605
Conti 1990	L. Conti (ed.), *Medicina e biologia nella rivoluzione scientifica*, Perugia 1990
Cortesi 1908	F. Cortesi, 'Il catalogo dell'erbario d'uno dei primi Lincei', *Annali di Botanica*, VI, 1908, pp. 153–6
Daléchamps 1586	J. Daléchamps, *Historia generalis plantarum*, Lyons 1586
Daubeny 1865	C. Daubeny, *Essay on the Trees and Shrubs of the Ancients*, Oxford and London, 1865
DBI	*Dizionario bibliografico degli italiani*, Istituto della Enciclopedia Italiana, I–, Rome 1960– (in progress)
de Angelis/ Lanzara 1986	G. de Angelis and P. Lanzara, 'La "Syntaxis Plantaria" di Federico Cesi nei codici di Parigi: la nascita della microscopia vegetale', in Cesi, *Atti* 1986, pp. 251–76
della Porta 1588	G.B. della Porta, *Phytognomonica*, Naples 1588
Dodoens 1569	R. Dodoens, *Florum, et coronarium odoratumque nonnullarum herbarum historia*, Antwerp 1569
Dodoens 1583	R. Dodoens, *Stirpium historia pemptades sex*, Antwerp 1583
Ferri 1997	S. Ferri (ed.), *Pietro Andrea Mattioli. Siena 1501–Trento 1578. La vita. Le opere*, Perugia 1997
Findlen 1990	P. Findlen, 'Jokes of nature and jokes of knowledge: the playfulness of scientific discourse in Early Modern Europe', *Renaissance Quarterly*, XLIII, 1990, pp. 292–331
Fiori cat. 2004	*Fiori. Cinque secoli di pittura floreale*, F. Solinas (ed.), exhib. cat., Biella 2004
Freedberg 1989	D. Freedberg, 'From Hebrew and gardens to oranges and lemons: Giovanni Battista Ferrari and Cassiano dal Pozzo', in *Cassiano dal Pozzo. Atti del seminario internazionale di studi*, Naples, 18–19 December 1987, F. Solinas (ed.), Rome 1989, pp. 37–72
Freedberg 1993	D. Freedberg, 'Cassiano and the art of natural history', in *Cassiano* cat. 1993, pp. 141–222
Freedberg 2002	D. Freedberg, *The Eye of the Lynx. Galileo, His Friends, and the Beginnings of Modern Natural History*, Chicago and London 2002
Fuchs 1542	L. Fuchs, *De historia stirpium commentarii insignes . . .* , Basle 1542
Gabrieli 1929	G. Gabrieli, 'Due codici iconografici di piante miniate nella Biblioteca Reale di Windsor', *Rendiconti dell'Accademia Nazionale dei Lincei. Classe di scienze fisiche, matematiche e naturali*, ser. X, VI, fasc. 10, 1929, pp. 531–8
Gabrieli 1938–42	G. Gabrieli, 'Il carteggio linceo della vecchia accademia di Federico Cesi (1603–1630)', *Atti della Reale Accademia dei Lincei, Memorie della classe di scienze morali, storiche e filologiche*, ser. VI, VII (fasc. 1–4, 1938–42), 1959, pp. 1–1446
Gabrieli 1989	G. Gabrieli, *Contributi alla storia dell'Accademia dei Lincei*, 2 vols, Rome 1989
Galilei 1890–1909	*Le opere di Galileo Galilei. Edizione nazionale*, A. Favaro (ed.), 20 vols, Florence 1890–1909
Garbari/Tongiorgi Tomasi/Tosi 2002	F. Garbari, L. Tongiorgi Tomasi and A. Tosi, *Giardino dei semplici / Garden of Simples*, Pisa 2002
Gerard 1597	J. Gerard, *The Herball or Generall Historie of Plantes*, London 1597
Guerrini 2006	L. Guerrini, *I trattati naturalistici di Federico Cesi*, Rome 2006
Hernández 1651	F. Hernández, *Rerum medicarum Novae Hispaniae thesaurus, seu, plantarum, animalium, mineralium Mexicanorum historia*, Rome 1651
Imperato 1599	F. Imperato, *Dell' historia naturale . . .* , Naples 1599
Lack 2001	H.W. Lack, *Garden of Eden*, Cologne, London, Madrid, New York and Tokyo 2001

Lazzeri 1996	G. Lazzeri, *L'erbario del frate dell'Eremo di Calomini*, Lucca 1996
Lenzi 1997	M.L. Lenzi, 'Dal "Regno di Iatria" alla corte di Praga', in Ferri 1997, pp. 83–104
Lincei cat. 2002–3	*Il trionfo sul tempo. Manoscritti illustrati dell'Accademia Nazionale dei Lincei*, A. Cadei (ed.), exhib. cat., Rome and Modena 2002–3
Mabberley *et al.* 2001	D.J. Mabberley, C.E. Jarvis and B.E. Juniper, 'The name of the apple', *Telopea*, IX (2), 2001, pp. 421–30
MacDougall 1994	E.B. MacDougall, 'A cardinal's bulb garden: A *giardino segreto* in the Palazzo Barberini in Rome', in *Fountains, Statues and Flowers. Studies in Italian Gardens of the Sixteenth and Seventeenth Centuries*, E.B. MacDougall, Washington D.C. 1994, pp. 219–342
Maclean 2002	I. Maclean, *Logic, Signs and Nature in the Renaissance. The Case of Learned Medicine*, Cambridge 2002
Mariotti MS	A. Mariotti, *Orti botanici dell'Università d'Italia*, Biblioteca Augusta di Perugia, Carte Mariotti, MS 1774, fols 1–2
Mariotti 1997	M.G. Mariotti, 'L'identificazione delle piante', in Ferri 1997, pp. 161–214
Marzell 1972	H. Marzell, *Wörterbuch des deutschen Pflanzennamen*, II, Leipzig 1972
Mattioli 1544	P.A. Mattioli, *Di Pedacio Dioscoride Anazarbeo libri cinque*, Venice 1544
Mattioli 1565	*Commentarii P.A. Matthioli in sex libros Pedacii Dioscoridis*, Venice 1565
Mattioli 1568	*I Discorsi di M. Pietro Andrea Matthioli . . . nelli sei libri di Pedacio Dioscoride Anazarbeo della materia medicinale*, Venice 1568
Meiggs 1982	R. Meiggs, *Trees and Timber in the Ancient Mediterranean World*, Oxford 1982
Monardes 1575	N. Monardes, *Delle cose che vengono portate dall'Indie Occidentali pertinenti all'uso della medicina*, Venice 1575
Morton 1990	T.M. Morton, *A Souvenir Album of Flowers from the Royal Collection*, London 1990
Moscardo 1651	L. Moscardo, *Note overo memorie del museo di Lodovico Moscardo*, Padua 1651
Olmi 1992	G. Olmi, *L'inventario del mondo. Catalogazione della natura e luoghi del sapere nella prima età moderna*, Bologna 1992
Pagel 1982	W. Pagel, *Joan Baptista Van Helmont: Reformer of Science and Medicine*, Cambridge 1982
Penzig 1905	O. Penzig, 'Illustrazione degli erbari di Gherardo Cibo', in *Contribuzioni alla Storia della Botanica*, Milan 1905, pp. 1–237
Pirotta 1904	R. Pirotta, *Sodales R. Lynceorum Academiae annum CCC ab eius institutione concelebrantes Fredeirici Cesi . . . opus probatissimum . . . Breve illustrazione delle Tabulae Phytosophicae di Federico Cesi*, Rome 1904
Quaderni Puteani 1	*Il museo cartaceo di Cassiano dal Pozzo. Cassiano naturalista. Quaderni Puteani* 1, Milan 1989
Quaderni Puteani 4	See *Cassiano* cat. 1993
Raimondi 1906	B. Raimondi, 'Lettere di P.A. Mattioli a Ulisse Aldrovandi', *Bullettino Senese di Storia Patria*, XIII, 1–2, 1906, pp. 1–67
Raimondi 1974	E. Raimondi, *Il romanzo senza idillio. Saggio sui 'Promessi Sposi'*, Turin 1974
Ramusio 1556	G.B. Ramusio, *Terzo volume delle navigationi et viaggi . . .*, Venice 1556
Riddle 1985	J.M. Riddle, *Dioscorides on Pharmacy and Medicine*, Austin, Tex, 1985
Rienstra 1968	M.H. Rienstra, 'Giovanni Ecchio Linceo. Appunti cronologici e bibliografici', *Atti dell'Accademia Nazionale dei Lincei. Rendiconti della classe di scienze morali, storiche e filologiche*, ser. VIII, XXIII, 1968, pp. 7–12 and 255–66
Salaman 1940	R.N. Salaman, 'Why "Jerusalem artichoke"?', *J Royal Horticultural Soc*, LXV (1940), pt X, pp. 388–48, pt xi, 376–83
Schott 1697	G. Schott, *Physica curiosa*, Würzburg 1697
Scott/Freedberg 2000	A.C. Scott and D. Freedberg, *The Paper Museum of Cassiano dal Pozzo. Fossil Woods and Other Geological Specimens*, Turnhout 2000

Solinas 1989 — F. Solinas, 'L'Erbario Miniato e altri fogli di iconografia botanica appartenuti a Cassiano dal Pozzo', in *Quaderni Puteani* 1, pp. 52–76

Tabernaemontanus 1590 — J. Theodorus, *Eicones plantarum seu stirpium*, Frankfurt 1590

Temkin 1973 — O. Temkin, *Galenism: Rise and Decline of a Medical Philosophy*, Ithaca, NY, 1973

Thevet 1575 — A. Thevet, *La cosmographie universelle*, 2 vols, Paris 1575

Thompson 1934 — C.J.S. Thompson, *The Mystic Mandrake*, London 1934

Tongiorgi Tomasi 1980 — L. Tongiorgi Tomasi, 'Il giardino dei semplici dello studio pisano. Collezionismo, scienza e immagine tra cinque e seicento', in *Livorno e Pisa: due città e un territorio nella politica dei Medici*, exhib. cat., Pisa 1980, pp. 514–26

Tongiorgi Tomasi 1986 — L. Tongiorgi Tomasi, 'Francesco Mingucci, "giardiniere" e pittore naturalista: un aspetto della committenza barberiniana nella Roma seicentesca', in Cesi, *Atti* 1986, pp. 277–306

Tongiorgi Tomasi 1994 — L. Tongiorgi Tomasi, 'Erbario', in *Enciclopedia dell'arte medievale*, v, Rome 1994, pp. 839–41

Tongiorgi Tomasi 1997 — L. Tongiorgi Tomasi, *An Oak Spring Flora. Flower Illustration from the Fifteenth Century to the Present Time. A Selection of the Rare Books, Manuscripts and Works of Art in the Collection of Rachel Lambert Mellon*, Upperville, Va 1997

Toresella 1992 — S. Toresella, 'Le prime piante americane negli erbari del cinquecento', *Le Scienze*, XLVIII/281, 1992, pp. 46–57

Turner 1568 — W. Turner, *The Thirde Parte of Guilliam Turners Herball*, Cologne 1568

Turner 1938 — D.M. Turner, 'The economic rhubarbs', *J Royal Horticultural Soc*, LXIII, pp. 355–70

Ubrizsy 1980 — A. Ubrizsy, 'Il codice micologico di Federico Cesi', *Atti dell'Accademia Nazionale dei Lincei. Rendiconti della classe di scienze fisiche, matematiche e naturali*, ser. VIII, LXVIII, 1980, pp. 129–34

L'Uccelliera 2000 — F. Solinas, *L'Uccelliera. Un libro di arte e scienza nella Roma dei primi lincei*, Florence 2000

Woodville 1790 — W. Woodville, *Medical Botany*, I, London 1790

CONCORDANCE A

Present locations, folio or inventory numbers and catalogue raisonné numbers of drawings in these two volumes

1. Royal Library, Windsor Castle

RL no.	Cat. no.	RL no.	Cat. no.	RL no.	Cat. no.	RL no.	Cat. no.
19365	**281**	27695	5	27738	**48**	27781	**91**
19375	**288**	27696	6	27739	**49**	27782	**92**
19384	**290**	27697	7	27740	**50**	27783	**93**
19387	**217**	27698	8	27741	**51**	27784	**94**
19388	**228**	27699	9	27742	**52**	27785	**95**
19389	**230**	27700	**10**	27743	**53**	27786	**96**
19390	**232**	27701	**11**	27744	**54**	27787	**97**
19391	**234**	27702	**12**	27745	**55**	27788	**98**
19392	**238**	27703	**13**	27746	**56**	27789	**99**
19393	**239**	27704	**14**	27747	**57**	27790	**100**
19394	**240**	27705	**15**	27748	**58**	27791	**101**
19395	**241**	27706	**16**	27749	**59**	27792	**102**
19396	**247**	27707	**17**	27750	**60**	27793	**103**
19397	**248**	27708	**18**	27751	**61**	27794	**104**
19398	**250**	27709	**19**	27752	**62**	27795	**105**
19399	**251**	27710	**20**	27753	**63**	27796	**106**
19400	**252**	27711	**21**	27754	**64**	27797	**107**
19401	**253**	27712	**22**	27755	**65**	27798	**108**
19402	**260**	27713	**23**	27756	**66**	27799	**109**
19403	**261**	27714	**24**	27757	**67**	27800	**110**
19404	**264**	27715	**25**	27758	**68**	27801	**111**
19405	**266**	27716	**26**	27759	**69**	27802	**112**
19406	**267**	27717	**27**	27760	**70**	27803	**113**
19407	**268**	27718	**28**	27761	**71**	27804	**114**
19408	**269**	27719	**29**	27762	**72**	27805	**115**
19409	**270**	27720	**30**	27763	**73**	27806	**116**
19410	**271**	27721	**31**	27764	**74**	27807	**117**
19411	**272**	27722	**32**	27765	**75**	27808	**118**
19412	**273**	27723	**33**	27766	**76**	27809	**119**
19413	**275**	27724	**34**	27767	**77**	27810	**120**
19414	**276**	27725	**35**	27768	**78**	27811	**121**
19415	**277**	27726	**36**	27769	**79**	27812	**122**
19453	**229**	27727	**37**	27770	**80**	27813	**123**
19454	**233**	27728	**38**	27771	**81**	27814	**124**
19455	**235**	27729	**39**	27772	**82**	27815	**125**
19456	**236**	27730	**40**	27773	**83**	27816	**126**
19457	**237**	27731	**41**	27774	**84**	27817	**127**
21143	**291**	27732	**42**	27775	**85**	27818	**128**
26526	**293**	27733	**43**	27776	**86**	27819	**129**
27691	**1**	27734	**44**	27777	**87**	27820	**130**
27692	**2**	27735	**45**	27778	**88**	27821	**131**
27693	**3**	27736	**46**	27779	**89**	27822	**132**
27694	**4**	27737	**47**	27780	**90**	27823	**133**

(Royal Library, Windsor Castle cont.)

RL no.	Cat. no.	RL no.	Cat. no.	RL no.	Cat. no.	RL no.	Cat. no.
27824	**134**	27845	**155**	27866	**176**	27887	**197**
27825	**135**	27846	**156**	27867	**177**	27888	**198**
27826	**136**	27847	**157**	27868	**178**	27889	**199**
27827	**137**	27848	**158**	27869	**179**	27890	**200**
27828	**138**	27849	**159**	27870	**180**	27891	**201**
27829	**139**	27850	**160**	27871	**181**	27892	**202**
27830	**140**	27851	**161**	27872	**182**	27893	**203**
27831	**141**	27852	**162**	27873	**183**	27894	**204**
27832	**142**	27853	**163**	27874	**184**	27895	**205**
27833	**143**	27854	**164**	27875	**185**	27896	**206**
27834	**144**	27855	**165**	27876	**186**	27897	**207**
27835	**145**	27856	**166**	27877	**187**	27898	**208**
27836	**146**	27857	**167**	27878	**188**	27899	**209**
27837	**147**	27858	**168**	27879	**189**	27900	**210**
27838	**148**	27859	**169**	27880	**190**	27901	**211**
27839	**149**	27860	**170**	27881	**191**	28738	**279**
27840	**150**	27861	**171**	27882	**192**	32569	**280**
27841	**151**	27862	**172**	27883	**193**	32571	**262**
27842	**152**	27863	**173**	27884	**194**		
27843	**153**	27864	**174**	27885	**195**		
27844	**154**	27865	**175**	27886	**196**		

2. Victoria and Albert Museum, London

Inv. no.	Cat. no.
E. 731-1949	**218**
E. 735-1949	**242**

3. Biblioteca dell'Accademia Nazionale dei Lincei e Corsiniana, Rome

Inv. no.	Cat. no.
Fondo A, 40bis	**222**
Fondo A, 40bis	**223**

4. Dispersed: Boone sale. Sotheby's New York, 16 September 1988, drawings from the estate of James R. Herbert Boone (see p. 49)

Lot no.	Cat. no.	Lot no.	Cat. no.	Lot no.	Cat. no.	Lot no.	Cat. no.
132	**215**	135	**221**	138	**246**	144	**279**
132	**254**	135	**227**	139	**231**	145	**225**
132	**255**	136	**212**	139	**274**	145	**226**
133	**243**	136	**258**	140	**287**	146	**278**
133	**244**	136	**263**	143	**222**	154	**282**
134	**256**	137	**283**	143	**223**		

CONCORDANCE B

Drawings with 'Pozzo' numbers in two distinct numerical sequences
(from the *Erbario Miniato* corpus and from other loose dal Pozzo botanical material),
with catalogue numbers

Erbario Miniato

'Pozzo' no.	Cat. no.	'Pozzo' no.	Cat. no.	'Pozzo' no.	Cat. no.	'Pozzo' no.	Cat. no.
279	**212**	*420*	**254**	*518*	**20**	*561*	**63**
282	**213**	*421*	**255**	*519*	**21**	*562*	**64**
283	**214**	*426*	**256**	*520*	**22**	*563*	**65**
284	**215**	*427*	**257**	*521*	**23**	*564*	**66**
285	**216**	*428*	**258**	*522*	**24**	*565*	**67**
287	**217**	*429*	**259**	*523*	**25**	*566*	**68**
288	**218**	*435*	**260**	*524*	**26**	*567*	**69**
289	**219**	*438*	**261**	*525*	**27**	*568*	**70**
290	**220**	*443*	**262**	*526*	**28**	*569*	**71**
292	**221**	*456*	**263**	*527*	**29**	*570*	**72**
293	**222**	*467*	**264**	*528*	**30**	*571*	**73**
295	**223**	*470*	**265**	*529*	**31**	*572*	**74**
296	**224**	*471*	**266**	*530*	**32**	*573*	**75**
297	**225**	*478*	**267**	*531*	**33**	*574*	**76**
298	**226**	*481*	**268**	*532*	**34**	*575*	**77**
299	**227**	*485*	**269**	*533*	**35**	*576*	**79**
311	**228**	*486*	**270**	*534*	**36**	*577*	**80**
315	**229**	*487*	**271**	*535*	**37**	*578*	**81**
320	**230**	*491*	**272**	*536*	**38**	*579*	**82**
323	**231**	*492*	**273**	*537*	**39**	*580*	**83**
324	**232**	*493*	**274**	*538*	**40**	*581*	**84**
332	**233**	*494*	**275**	*539*	**41**	*582*	**85**
335	**234**	*497*	**276**	*540*	**42**	*583*	**86**
338	**235**	*498*	**277**	*541*	**43**	*584*	**87**
339	**236**	*499*	**1**	*542*	**44**	*585*	**88**
340	**237**	*500*	**2**	*543*	**45**	*586*	**89**
354	**238**	*501*	**3**	*544*	**46**	*587*	**90**
357	**239**	*502*	**4**	*545*	**47**	*588*	**91**
369	**240**	*503*	**5**	*546*	**48**	*589*	**92**
371	**241**	*504*	**6**	*547*	**49**	*590*	**93**
384	**242**	*505*	**7**	*548*	**50**	*591*	**94**
387	**242a**	*506*	**8**	*549*	**51**	*592*	**95**
388	**243**	*507*	**9**	*550*	**52**	*593*	**96**
388	**244**	*508*	**10**	*551*	**53**	*594*	**97**
391	**245**	*509*	**11**	*552*	**54**	*595*	**98**
392	**246**	*510*	**12**	*553*	**55**	*596*	**99**
401	**247**	*511*	**13**	*554*	**56**	*597*	**100**
404	**248**	*512*	**14**	*555*	**57**	*598*	**101**
414	**249**	*513*	**15**	*556*	**58**	*599*	**102**
415	**250**	*514*	**16**	*557*	**59**	*600*	**103**
416	**251**	*515*	**17**	*558*	**60**	*601*	**104**
417	**252**	*516*	**18**	*559*	**61**	*602*	**105**
419	**253**	*517*	**19**	*560*	**62**	*603*	**106**

(*Erbario Miniato* cont.)

'Pozzo' no.	Cat. no.	'Pozzo' no.	Cat. no.	'Pozzo' no.	Cat. no.	'Pozzo' no.	Cat. no.
604	**107**	*630*	**133**	*656*	**160**	*682*	**186**
605	**108**	*631*	**134**	*657*	**161**	*683*	**187**
606	**109**	*632*	**135**	*658*	**162**	*684*	**188**
607	**110**	*633*	**136**	*659*	**163**	*685*	**189**
608	**111**	*634*	**137**	*660*	**164**	*686*	**190**
609	**112**	*635*	**138**	*661*	**165**	*687*	**191**
610	**113**	*636*	**139**	*662*	**166**	*688*	**192**
611	**114**	*637*	**140**	*663*	**167**	*689*	**193**
612	**115**	*638*	**141**	*664*	**168**	*690*	**194**
613	**116**	*639*	**142**	*665*	**169**	*691*	**195**
614	**117**	*640*	**143**	*666*	**170**	*692*	**196**
615	**118**	*641*	**144**	*667*	**171**	*693*	**198**
616	**119**	*642*	**145**	*668*	**172**	*694*	**199**
617	**120**	*643*	**146**	*669*	**173**	*695*	**200**
618	**121**	*644*	**147**	*670*	**174**	*697*	**202**
619	**122**	*645*	**148**	*671*	**175**	*698*	**203**
620	**123**	*646*	**149**	*672*	**176**	*699*	**204**
621	**124**	*647*	**150**	*673*	**177**	*700*	**205**
622	**125**	*648*	**151**	*674*	**178**	*701*	**206**
623	**126**	*649*	**152**	*675*	**179**	*702*	**207**
624	**127**	*650*	**153**	*676*	**180**	*703*	**208**
625	**128**	*651*	**154**	*677*	**181**	*704*	**209**
626	**129**	*652*	**155**	*678*	**182**	*705*	**210**
627	**130**	*653*	**156**	*679*	**183**		
628	**131**	*654*	**157**	*680*	**184**		
629	**132**	*655*	**159**	*681*	**185**		

Other dal Pozzo botanical drawings

'Pozzo' no.	Cat. no.
216	**278**
382	**279**
388	**280**
426	**281**
523	**282**
562	**283**
563	**283**
598	**284**
599	**284**
603	**285**
604	**286**
801	**287**
984	**288**

INDEX OF SCIENTIFIC AND ENGLISH COMMON NAMES

All references are to catalogue numbers. Also included are cross-references to drawings of mycological material in the Paper Museum already published (Part B.II *Fungi*). For the ease of reference of Italian readers, an index of Italian common names follows.

INDEX OF ITALIAN COMMON NAMES

GENERAL INDEX

Page numbers in *italics* denote illustrations. The letter 'n' following a page number indicates that the reference will be found in a note.

LIST OF TEXT FIGURES

LIST OF COMPARATIVE FIGURES

PHOTOGRAPHIC ACKNOWLEDGEMENTS

All items in the Royal Collection are © 2007 HM Queen Elizabeth II. We are also grateful for permission to reproduce items in the following collections:

London, British Library: Figs 5, 8–9, 13–14

London, Victoria and Albert Museum: Cats **218**, **242**

London, The Warburg Institute: Comp. fig. 280

London, The Wellcome Trust Medical Photographic Library: Figs 6–7, 10, 15, 17, Comp. figs 242a and 293

Montpellier, Bibliothèque de l'École de Médecine: Fig. 12

New York, Arader Galleries: Cat. **282**

Paris, Bibliothèque de l'Institut de France/RMN: Figs 18–21

Pisa, Biblioteca Universitaria: Comp. fig. 160

Rome, Accademia Nazionale dei Lincei: Cats **222–223**, Figs 2, 11

Vienna, Österreichische Nationalbibliothek: Fig. 4

Every effort has been made to contact copyright holders; any omissions are inadvertent, and will be corrected in future editions if notification of the amended credit is sent to the publisher in writing.